Dr. C's

Ultimate

2022

PENNSYLVANIA

MPJE

REVIEW

MASTERING THE MPJE COMPETENCIES

GARY CACCIATORE, Pharm.D., J.D.

Published by Dr. C's Review Guides
www.mpjereviews.com
info@mpjereviews.com

January 2022

ISBN 978-0-578-32490-6

CONTENTS

INTRODUCTION

Dr. C's Ultimate Pennsylvania MPJE® Review 2022 provides an overview of state and federal law impacting the practice of pharmacy in Pennsylvania. Although primarily intended to serve as a study guide for the Pennsylvania Multistate Pharmacy Jurisprudence Exam (MPJE®), the book also serves as an excellent reference book on Pennsylvania pharmacy law by reorganizing and summarizing the statutes and rules in a more comprehensible manner.

The book includes explanatory notes to help the reader make sense of often confusing or ambiguous statutory and rule language, and groups different rules and statutes together based on subject matter to better facilitate learning. *Study Tips* are provided throughout the book to note important material and help clarify information that is often misunderstood or causes confusion.

As you experienced when you were a pharmacy student, a recent graduate, or a seasoned pharmacist who last sat for an exam more than a few years ago, your study plan and preparation are critical to your success. The Pennsylvania MPJE requires you to fully comprehend state and federal laws, regulations, and a pharmacist's responsibilities.

Dr. C's Ultimate Pennsylvania MPJE® Review has been developed by pharmacy regulatory experts with education and experience in both law and pharmacy. The book is designed to assist you in focusing on the elements of the exam that may appear on the Pennsylvania MPJE, although the author and content experts have no specific knowledge of questions that are on the exam. All references to sections of statute refer to the Pennsylvania Pharmacy Act (PPA) unless otherwise specified.

The key to success is to allow adequate time in your study plan to review parts of the law that are least familiar to you. We believe this book will help in the process and support your successful exam completion.

*MPJE is a registered trademark of the National Association of Boards of Pharmacy

ABOUT THE AUTHOR

Gary Cacciatore, Pharm.D., J.D.

Gary Cacciatore is the founder and President of Dr. C's Review Guides. In 2021, he retired from Cardinal Health, where he served as Associate Regulatory Counsel and Vice President of Regulatory Affairs. Prior to joining Cardinal Health, Dr. Cacciatore was an Assistant Professor at the University of Houston College of Pharmacy and the University of Houston Law Center, where he taught courses in pharmacy law and ethics, drug information, and food and drug law. He currently serves as an Adjunct Associate Professor at the University of Houston College of Pharmacy and as an Adjunct Associate Professor at the University of Florida College of Pharmacy.

Dr. Cacciatore is the coauthor of *Texas and Federal Pharmacy and Drug Law*, a comprehensive textbook used by nearly all of the pharmacy schools in Texas, and *The Ultimate Texas MPJE Review Guide*, the leading Texas MPJE review book, which has been utilized by pharmacists and students from all 50 states and 10 foreign countries. He is also the author of *Dr. C's Ultimate Florida MPJE Review* and *Dr. C's Ultimate Federal Pharmacy Law Review*.

Dr. Cacciatore received his Doctor of Pharmacy degree with high honors from the University of Florida College of Pharmacy. He earned his Doctor of Jurisprudence degree with honors from the University of Houston Law Center. He is a past President of the American Society for Pharmacy Law (ASPL), and in 2015, he received the Joseph L. Fink III Founders Award from ASPL for outstanding and sustained contributions to the professions of pharmacy and law. Dr. Cacciatore was named the Outstanding Alumnus by the University of Florida College of Pharmacy for 2021.

Dr. Cacciatore is admitted to the bar in Texas and is a registered pharmacist in Texas and Florida.

ACKNOWLEDGEMENT

A special thank you to Kimberly Burns, R.Ph., J.D., for her contributions to and review of the Pennsylvania-specific content used within this book. Professor Burns is admitted to the bar in Pennsylvania and has been a practicing pharmacist in Pennsylvania for over 25 years. In addition, she has taught Federal and Pennsylvania Pharmacy Law courses to thousands of pharmacy students since 2002. Thanks to Professor Burns's knowledge and understanding of the pharmacy laws in Pennsylvania, she was able to assist in providing the relevant information required for the state-specific chapters of this book.

ACRONYMS

Most acronyms are defined the first time they are used in this book (and often several times), but here is a list of some of the major acronyms used:

ACPE	Accreditation Council for Pharmacy Education
CE	Continuing Education
CEU	Continuing Education Unit
CFR	Code of Federal Regulations
cGMP	Current Good Manufacturing Practices
CNM	Certified Nurse Midwife
CRNP	Certified Registered Nurse Practitioner
DEA	Drug Enforcement Administration
FCSA	Federal Controlled Substances Act (also may be listed as CSA)
FDA	Food and Drug Administration
FDCA	Food, Drug, and Cosmetic Act (Federal)
GMP	Good Manufacturing Practices
HIPAA	Health Insurance Portability and Accountability Act
LTCF	Long Term Care Facility
MPJE	Multistate Pharmacy Jurisprudence Exam
NABP	National Association of Boards of Pharmacy
NAPLEX	North American Pharmacist Licensure Exam
NDC	National Drug Code
OTC	Over-the-counter
PA	Physician Assistant
Pa. Code	Pennsylvania Administrative Code or Pennsylvania Code
PBOP	Pennsylvania Board of Pharmacy
PCSDDCA	Pennsylvania Controlled Substance, Drug, Device, and Cosmetic Act
PCSDDCR	Pennsylvania Controlled Substance, Drug, Device, and Cosmetic Regulations
PDMP	Prescription Drug Monitoring Program
PPA	Pennsylvania Pharmacy Act
PPI	Patient Package Insert
PPPA	Poison Prevention Packaging Act
REMS	Risk Evaluation and Mitigation Strategies
USP	United States Pharmacopeia

Information on the Multistate Pharmacy Jurisprudence Exam (MPJE®)

General Information

NABP Website (nabp.pharmacy) and the NAPLEX/MPJE Registration Bulletin

Detailed information on the MPJE is available from the National Association of Boards of Pharmacy (NABP) on its website under Programs and Exams, as well as in the NAPLEX/MPJE Candidate Application Bulletin, which is available for download on the website. The NABP website and the bulletin contain detailed information on registering for the exam, scheduling testing appointments, fees, identification requirements, security measures, question types, and score results. Candidates should download and read the Candidate Application Bulletin carefully as well as visit the NABP website for additional information specific to the MPJE.

Exam Content and Structure

The MPJE is a 120-item computer-based examination that uses adaptive technology. This means the computer adapts the questions you receive based on your previous responses. You are allowed 2 and 1/2 hours to complete the exam. You must complete 107 questions for your exam to be scored. Of the 120 items on the exam, 100 count toward your score. The questions not counting toward your score are being pretested; however, you will not know which questions count toward your score and which questions are being pretested. Because it is a computer-based examination, you cannot go back and review a question or change an answer once you have confirmed it and moved to the next question. You also cannot skip a question. Since there is a penalty for unanswered questions, you should answer all the questions.

The exam content and questions are developed by Board of Pharmacy representatives, practitioners, and educators from around the country who serve as item writers. Each state Board of Pharmacy approves the questions that are used for its particular state.

Previously results were reported on a scaled score and candidates had to achieve a score of 75 to pass the exam. This is not 75%, but a scaled score whereby your performance is measured against predetermined minimum abilities. NABP no longer reports actual scores. Scores are only reported as pass or fail and results are generally provided 7 business days after taking the exam. Candidates are allowed five attempts to pass the exam.

While you must have a good base knowledge of the laws and rules governing the practice of pharmacy in your state, simply memorizing the laws will not suffice. The exam is not simply questions that ask you to identify or repeat the law. There are many situational questions that will require you to apply the law to the facts provided. These types of questions are not as easy. When approaching these types of questions, it is helpful to remember that the goal of the Board of Pharmacy is to protect the public health. Answers that address that goal are most likely to be correct. At the same time, the Board of Pharmacy must also enforce the laws, so many of the laws and rules are intended to assist the Board with that function. Rules related to recordkeeping and documentation are especially important to boards of pharmacy to help them identify who or what caused an error in a pharmacy that may cause patient harm. Keeping these functions of the boards of pharmacy in mind may help you when trying to choose between answers on the exam. The MPJE consists of several types of questions, including multiple choice, multiple response (i.e., select all that apply), and ordered response. When the MPJE began using multiple response questions, they no longer needed to write multiple choice questions that were K-type questions. K-type questions are multiple choice questions where the answer choices consist of different combinations of the available choices. For example, choice A is I only, choice B is I and III, choice C is II and IV, and choice D is I, II, and III. Although new questions on the MPJE are not K-type questions, there are likely still many older questions that are K-type questions, so you should not be surprised to see these types of questions. Examples of each question type are provided below:

Multiple Choice Sample Question

A Pennsylvania pharmacist must obtain how many continuing education (CE) hours to renew his or her license in each renewal period?

a. 15 hours
b. 20 hours
c. 30 hours
d. 40 hours

Multiple Response Sample Question

Which are permissible ways for a pharmacist to obtain continuing education? Select all that apply.

_____ Completing an ACPE-accredited continuing education course online
_____ Attending a live meeting that offers ACPE-accredited continuing education credits
_____ Auditing a course at a College of Pharmacy
_____ Performing volunteer services to the indigent within the state

STUDY TIP: When answering multiple response questions, it is recommended that you choose more than one answer. If only one answer is correct, it is more likely to be a multiple choice question.

Ordered Response Sample Question

Place the following products in order from the least abuse potential to the greatest abuse potential. (All options must be used.) Left-click the mouse to highlight, drag, and order the answer options.

Unordered Options	Ordered Response
Tylenol with Codeine	_____
Sudafed	_____
Valium	_____
Vicodin	_____

STUDY TIP: Make sure you read the ordered response question carefully and put the items in the correct order, not the reverse order. Double-check the order before hitting the Submit button.

Basic Study and Preparation Tips

Below are helpful study and preparation tips to consider for the MPJE:

- Read and review relevant laws, regulations, and available government resources.
- Revisit pharmacy law course materials from pharmacy school (if recent graduate) and update information.
- When completing any practice questions, make sure you understand the concept and why the correct answer is correct and the other options are incorrect.
- Make and memorize charts and lists (i.e., label requirements, quantities, time frames).
- Be prepared to read exam directions and questions carefully and recall applicable laws.
- Be prepared to apply knowledge and skills of relevant laws and regulations.
- Be prepared to select the best answer. Do not overanalyze the questions or focus on the very rare instances that may change the answer.
- Be prepared to use time management skills during the exam (approximately 1.25 minutes per question).
- Do not rely on what your own work environment does. Your employer may have additional or stricter policies, but you must answer exam questions based on the legal and regulatory requirements.
- Do not overlook important words such as "must," "can," "should," and "may."
- Do not forget to consider federal and state laws, choosing the stricter requirement when both apply.
- Do your best to remain relaxed and focused.

Federal Versus State Law

When comparing federal law versus state law, the general rule is to always follow the stricter law. In the rare instance where state and federal law directly conflict so that you cannot follow one without violating the other, the federal law would prevail. It is important to understand that **no distinction is made on the MPJE exam between federal and state law questions**. You should answer each question in terms of the prevailing laws of the state in which you are seeking licensure, which for purposes of this book is Pennsylvania.

This means that you should not see a question on the exam that starts out with the words "According to the Federal Controlled Substances Act . . ." Such a question would not be valid because it is asking you to answer the question based on federal law only. If Pennsylvania has a law that is different and stricter than the federal law, that is the law that must be followed and would be the correct answer.

Pre-MPJE

NABP offers a Pre-MPJE exam that candidates can register to take online at NABP's website. This is the only practice exam that features valid questions from previous versions of the MPJE. The exam consists of 40 questions, and 50 minutes are allotted to complete the exam. The Pre-MPJE can be taken only one time for each jurisdiction a person is seeking licensure in. The official NABP Pre-MPJE exam can be taken only on the NABP website. There are other websites using the term "Pre-MPJE" that are not affiliated with NABP.

MPJE Competency Statements

Each question on the MPJE is tied to a specific competency statement. The competency statements for the MPJE can be accessed on NABP's website, and we have also included them in this section for your reference. You must master a certain number of competencies to pass the exam. It is possible that you will have to answer more than one question correctly in order to pass a particular competency, depending on the difficulty of the questions. So you may see more than one question on a single topic. In addition, you may get a similar question or questions from the same competency because one or more of those questions are being pretested and do not count toward your score. It is imperative that you read through the competency statements in the registration bulletin, although not every competency statement is covered under Pennsylvania law.

Note: At the time of publication of this book, NABP was in the process of redrafting the MPJE Competencies. Readers should check the NABP website and Candidate Application Bulletin for the current version of the MPJE Competencies.

MPJE® Competency Statements

Area 1 | Pharmacy Practice (83%)

1.1 **Legal responsibilities of the pharmacist and other pharmacy personnel**

1.1.1 Unique legal responsibilities of the pharmacist-in-charge (or equivalent), pharmacists, interns, and pharmacy owners

Responsibilities for inventory, loss and/or theft of prescription drugs, the destruction/disposal of prescription drugs, and the precedence of Local, State, or Federal requirements

1.1.2 Qualifications, scope of duties, and conditions for practice relating to pharmacy technicians and all other non-pharmacist personnel

Personnel ratios, duties, tasks, roles, and functions of non-pharmacist personnel

1.2 **Requirements for the acquisition and distribution of pharmaceutical products, including samples**

1.2.1 Requirements and recordkeeping in relation to the ordering, acquiring, and maintenance of all pharmaceutical products and bulk drug substances/excipients

Legitimate suppliers, pedigrees, and the maintenance of acquisition records

1.2.2 Requirements for distributing pharmaceutical products and preparations, including the content and maintenance of distribution records

Legal possession of pharmaceutical products (including drug samples), labeling, packaging, repackaging, compounding, and sales to practitioners

1.3 **Legal requirements that must be observed in the issuance of a prescription/drug order**

1.3.1 Prescription/order requirements for pharmaceutical products and the limitations on their respective therapeutic uses

Products, preparations, their uses, and limitations applicable to all prescribed orders for both human and veterinary uses

1.3.2 Scope of authority, scope of practice, and valid registration of all practitioners who are authorized under law to prescribe, dispense, or administer pharmaceutical products, including controlled substances

Federal and State registrations, methadone programs, office-based opioid treatment programs, regulations related to retired or deceased prescribers, internet prescribing, and limits on jurisdictional prescribing

1.3.3 Conditions under which the pharmacist participates in the administration of pharmaceutical products or in the management of patients' drug therapy

Prescriptive authority, collaborative practice, consulting, counseling, medication administration (including immunizations and vaccines), ordering labs, medication therapy management, and disease state management

1.3.4 Requirements for issuing a prescription/order

Content and format for written, telephonic voice transmission, electronic facsimile, computer and internet, during emergency conditions, and tamper-resistant prescription forms

1.3.5 Requirements for the issuance of controlled substance prescriptions/orders

Content and format for written, telephonic voice transmission, electronic facsimile, computerized and internet, during emergency conditions, conditions for changing a prescription, time limits for dispensing initial prescriptions/drug orders, and requirements for multiple Schedule II orders

1.3.6 Limits of a practitioner's authority to authorize refills of a pharmaceutical product, including controlled substances

1.4 **Procedures necessary to properly dispense a pharmaceutical product, including controlled substances, pursuant to a prescription/drug order**

1.4.1 Responsibilities for determining whether prescriptions/orders were issued for a legitimate medical purpose and within all applicable legal restrictions

Corresponding responsibility, maximum quantities, restricted distribution systems, red flags/automated alerts, controlled substances, valid patient/prescriber relationship, and due diligence to ensure validity of the order

1.4.2 Requirements for the transfer of existing prescription/order information from one pharmacist to another

1.4.3 Conditions under which a prescription/order may be filled or refilled

Emergency fills or refills, partial dispensing of a controlled substance, disaster or emergency protocol, patient identification, requirement for death with dignity, medical marijuana, and conscience/moral circumstances

1.4.4 Conditions under which prospective drug use review is conducted prior to dispensing

Patient-specific therapy and requirements for patient-specific documentation

1.4.5 Conditions under which product selection is permitted or mandated

Consent of the patient and/or prescriber, passing-on of cost savings, and appropriate documentation

1.4.6 Requirements for the labeling of pharmaceutical products and preparations dispensed pursuant to a prescription/order

Generic and therapeutic equivalency, formulary use, auxiliary labels, patient package inserts, FDA medication guides, and written drug information

1.4.7 Packaging requirements of pharmaceutical products, preparations, and devices to be dispensed pursuant to a prescription/order

Child-resistant and customized patient medication packaging

1.4.8 Conditions under which a pharmaceutical product, preparation, or device may not be dispensed

Adulteration, misbranding, and dating

1.4.9 Requirements for compounding pharmaceutical products

Environmental controls, release checks and testing, beyond use date (BUD), and initial and ongoing training

1.4.10 Requirements for emergency kits

Supplying, maintenance, access, security, and inventory

Pseudoephedrine, dextromethorphan, emergency contraception, and behind-the-counter products, as appropriate

1.7 **Procedures for keeping records of information related to pharmacy practice, pharmaceutical products, and patients, including requirements for protecting patient confidentiality**

1.7.1 Requirements pertaining to controlled substance inventories

1.7.2 Content, maintenance, storage, and reporting requirements for records required in the operation of a pharmacy

Prescription filing systems, computer systems and backups, and prescription monitoring programs

1.7.3 Requirements for protecting patient confidentiality and confidential health records

HIPAA requirements and conditions for access and use of information

1.8 **Requirements for handling hazardous materials such as described in USP 800**

1.8.1 Requirements for appropriate disposal of hazardous materials

1.8.2 Requirements for training regarding hazardous materials

Reverse distributors, quarantine procedures, comprehensive safety programs, and Material Safety Data Sheets

1.8.3 Environmental controls addressing the proper storage, handling, and disposal of hazardous materials

Ventilation controls, personal protective equipment, work practices, and reporting

1.8.4 Methods for the compounding, dispensing, and administration of hazardous materials

All hazardous materials including sterile and non-sterile compounding

Area 2 | Licensure, Registration, Certification, and Operational Requirements (15%)

2.1 **Qualifications, application procedure, necessary examinations, and internship for licensure, registration, or certification**

of individuals engaged in the storage, distribution, and/or dispensing of pharmaceutical products (prescription and nonprescription)

2.1.1 Requirements for special or restricted licenses, registration, authorization, or certificates

Pharmacists, pharmacist preceptors, pharmacy interns, pharmacy technicians, controlled substance registrants, and under specialty pharmacist licenses (Nuclear, Consultant, etc.)

2.1.2 Standards of practice related to the practice of pharmacy

Quality assurance programs (including peer review), changing dosage forms, therapeutic substitution, error reporting, public health reporting requirements (such as notification of potential terrorist event, physical abuse, and treatment for tuberculosis), and issues of conscience and maintaining competency

2.1.3 Requirements for classifications and processes of disciplinary actions that may be taken against a registered, licensed, certified, or permitted individual

2.1.4 Requirements for reporting to and participating in programs addressing the inability of an individual licensed, registered, or certified by the Board to engage in the practice of pharmacy with reasonable skill and safety

Impairment caused by the use of alcohol, drugs, chemicals, or other materials, or mental, physical, or psychological conditions

2.2 **Requirements and application procedure for the registration, licensure, certification, or permitting of a practice setting or business entity**

2.2.1 Requirements for registration, license, certification, or permitting of a practice setting

In-state pharmacies, out-of-state pharmacies, specialty pharmacies, controlled substance registrants, wholesalers, distributors, manufacturers/repackagers, computer services providers, and internet pharmacies

2.2.2 Requirements for an inspection of a licensed, registered, certified, or permitted practice setting

2.2.3 Requirements for the renewal or reinstatement of a license, registration, certificate, or permit of a practice setting

2.2.4 Classifications and processes of disciplinary actions that may be taken against a registered, licensed, certified, or permitted practice setting

2.3 **Operational requirements for a registered, licensed, certified, or permitted practice setting**

2.3.1 Requirements for the operation of a pharmacy or practice setting that is not directly related to the dispensing of pharmaceutical products

Issues related to space, equipment, advertising and signage, security (including temporary absences of the pharmacist), policies and procedures, libraries, and references (including veterinary), and the display of licenses

2.3.2 Requirements for the possession, storage, and handling of pharmaceutical products, preparations, bulk drug substances/excipients, and devices, including controlled substances

Investigational new drugs, repackaged or resold drugs, sample pharmaceuticals, recalls, and outdated pharmaceutical products

2.3.3 Requirements for delivery of pharmaceutical products, preparations, bulk drug substances/excipients, and devices, including controlled substances

Issues related to identification of the person accepting delivery of a drug, use of the mail, contract delivery, use of couriers, use of pharmacy employees, use of kiosks, secure mailboxes, and script centers, use of vacuum tubes, and use of drive-up windows

Area 3 | General Regulatory Processes (2%)

3.1 **Application of regulations**

3.1.1 Laws and rules that regulate or affect the manufacture, storage, distribution, and dispensing of pharmaceutical products, preparations, bulk drug substances/excipients, and devices (prescription and nonprescription), including controlled substances

Food, Drug, and Cosmetic Act(s) and Regulations, the Controlled Substances Act(s) and Regulations, OBRA 90's Title IV Requirements,

Practice Acts and Rules, other statutes and regulations, including, but not limited to, dispensing of methadone, child-resistant packaging, tamper-resistant packaging, drug paraphernalia, drug samples, pharmacist responsibilities in Medicare-certified skilled-nursing facilities, NDC numbers, and schedules of controlled substances

CHAPTER ONE
Federal Food, Drug, and Cosmetic Act (FDCA), Poison Prevention Packaging Act (PPPA), and Other Miscellaneous Federal Laws

CHAPTER ONE

Federal Food, Drug, and Cosmetic Act (FDCA), Poison Prevention Packaging Act (PPPA), and Other Miscellaneous Federal Laws

I.   **Federal Food, Drug, and Cosmetic Act (FDCA) and Major Amendments**
   A.   Food, Drug, and Cosmetic Act of 1938
       1.   Following deaths caused by sulfanilamide elixir in 1937, Congress passed the first legislation that required new drugs to be proven safe prior to marketing.
       2.   Established the FDA and is the primary federal law dealing with food, drug, cosmetic, and medical device safety today (with many amendments).
   B.   Durham-Humphrey Amendment of 1951
       1.   Established two classes of drugs: prescription and over-the-counter (OTC).

STUDY TIP: You are expected to know those pharmaceutical products that require a prescription. It is particularly important to know that certain products in the same drug class may be either prescription or nonprescription depending on the product or the strength. For example, some insulin products are non-prescription; however, certain other insulin products such as Lantus® and Humalog® are prescription-only products. Another example is that ibuprofen 400 mg, 600 mg, and 800 mg products require a prescription, while ibuprofen 200 mg products do not.

---

       2.   Authorized verbal prescriptions and prescription refills.
   C.   Kefauver-Harris Amendments of 1962
       1.   Required new drugs be proven safe and effective for their claimed use. Prior to this amendment, new drugs only had to be safe. This amendment required new drugs to also be effective for their stated use.
       2.   Increased safety requirements for drugs and established Good Manufacturing Practices (GMPs) for manufacturing of drugs.
       3.   Gave FDA jurisdiction over prescription drug advertising.

D. Prescription Drug Marketing Act of 1987 (PDMA)

    1. Bans the re-importation of prescription drugs and insulin products produced in the United States (except by the manufacturer).

Note: This prohibition is on the re-importation of drugs produced in the United States and then exported. This is different from the importation of drugs manufactured in another country. Importation of drugs is generally prohibited; however, the Medicine Equity and Drug Safety (MEDS) Act of 2000 and the Medicare Prescription Drug, Improvement, and Modernization Act of 2003 both have provisions that allow importation of drugs under specific conditions. One of those conditions is that the Secretary of Health and Human Services (HHS) must certify to Congress that such imports do not threaten the health and safety of the American public and provide cost savings. FDA finalized new rules on importation on September 24, 2020, which permit states to serve as sponsors to import drugs from Canada under certain conditions.

    2. Bans the sale, trade, or purchase of prescription drug samples.

STUDY TIP: The Pennsylvania Pharmacy Act (PPA) (63 P. S. § 390-8(9)) is consistent with federal law, providing that it is unlawful for any person to buy, sell, cause to be sold, or offer for sale any drug or device whose packaging contains the inscription "sample" or "not for resale."

---

    3. Mandates the storage, handling, and recordkeeping requirements for prescription drug samples.

        a. These include obtaining written requests for samples from practitioners and requiring signatures of practitioners upon receipt.

        b. Samples may only be provided to practitioners or, upon request of a licensed practitioner, to an institutional pharmacy or to pharmacies of other healthcare facilities.

        c. Community pharmacies should not possess prescription drug samples, except for prescription drugs that may be ordered by a pharmacist. The only exception to this would be a community pharmacy that is part of a healthcare entity such as a community pharmacy owned by a hospital.

4. Prohibits, with certain exceptions, the resale of prescription drugs purchased by hospitals or healthcare facilities.
Note: This is intended to prevent diversion of drugs due to price differences because hospitals generally receive lower prices for drugs than community pharmacies.

E. The Drug Quality and Security Act (DQSA) of 2013—These amendments to the FDCA addressed two primary topics: large-scale compounding by pharmacies and establishment of a framework for a uniform track-and-trace system for prescription drugs throughout the supply chain to prevent counterfeit drugs.

1. Drug Compounding Quality Act (DCQA).

a. Passed in response to an outbreak of fungal meningitis in over 20 states in the fall of 2012, which was traced to a contaminated injectable steroid produced by the New England Compounding Center. This outbreak resulted in the death of over 60 patients and over 750 cases of infection.

b. Outsourcing facilities, often referred to as 503B facilities, are permitted to compound sterile products without receiving patient-specific prescriptions or medication orders. They are primarily regulated by FDA and are subject to FDA's current Good Manufacturing Practices (cGMPs).
Note: Despite this law being passed in 2013, there are currently only approximately 70 registered outsourcing facilities in the entire country.

c. Compounding pharmacies that are not registered with FDA as an "outsourcing facility" are often referred to as 503A facilities or 503A pharmacies and may only compound products pursuant to an individual prescription or medication order. They are permitted to do limited anticipatory compounding, are primarily regulated by the states, and are subject to USP Chapter 797 and Chapter 795 quality standards for sterile and nonsterile compounding respectively.

d. Outsourcing facilities that meet the Act's requirements are exempt from the premarket approval requirements for new drugs (FDCA Section 505), adequate directions for use requirements (FDCA Section 502(f)(1)), and drug track-and-trace provisions (FDCA Section 582).
Note: 503B outsourcing facilities are not exempt from good manufacturing practices, while 503A pharmacies are.

e. Outsourcing facilities must:
   (1) Have a licensed pharmacist who provides direct oversight over the drugs compounded;
   (2) Register as an outsourcing facility. The FDA website provides a list of the names of each outsourcing facility, along with the state where the facility is located, whether the facility compounds from bulk drug substances, and whether drugs compounded from bulk are sterile or nonsterile;
   (3) Report to the Secretary of HHS upon registering, and every six months thereafter, the drugs sold in the previous six months;
   (4) Be inspected by FDA according to a risk-based inspection schedule and pay annual fees to support it;
   (5) Report serious adverse event experiences within 15 days and conduct a follow-up investigation and reporting similar to current drug manufacturers; and
   (6) Label products with a statement identifying them as a compounded drug and other specified information about the drug.

f. Outsourcing facilities may not compound a drug product that includes a bulk drug substance unless:
   (1) The bulk drug substance appears on a list identifying bulk drug substances for which there is a clinical need (the 503B bulks list); or
   (2) The drug product compounded from such bulk drug substance appears on FDA's drug shortage list at the time of compounding, distribution, and dispensing.

Note: Bulk drug substances must be accompanied by a valid certificate of analysis and must have been manufactured by an establishment registered with FDA. In addition, if an applicable United States Pharmacopeia (USP) or National Formulary monograph exists, bulk drug substances must comply with the monograph. FDA issued an Interim Policy on Compounding Using Bulk Drug Substances under Section 503B of the FDCA, which is in place while the FDA develops the 503B bulks list. See the compounding section of FDA's website for more information.

g. Interstate distribution of compounded drugs from a 503A pharmacy.

   (1) Section 503A also limits interstate distribution of compounded drugs to 5% unless the compounder is located in a state that has entered into a memorandum of understanding (MOU) with FDA addressing inordinate amounts of compounded drugs in interstate commerce and providing for appropriate investigation of complaints by a state.

   (2) In states that have entered into an MOU with FDA, a pharmacy is considered to have distributed an inordinate amount of compounded drug products in interstate commerce if the number of prescription orders for compounded human drug products that the pharmacy distributed interstate during any calendar year is greater than 50% of the sum of:

      (i) the number of prescription orders for compounded human drug products that the pharmacy sent out of (or caused to be sent out of) the facility in which the drug products were compounded during that same calendar year; plus

      (ii) the number of prescription orders for compounded human drug products that were dispensed (e.g., picked up by a patient) at the pharmacy during that same calendar year.

Note: All of the compounded drugs must still be prepared based on an individually identified patient. Details on how these calculations are made can be found on the compounding page on FDA's website and in FDA's Standard MOU.

(3) In states that have not entered into an MOU with FDA, a pharmacy may not distribute (or cause to be distributed) compounded drug products out of the state in which they are compounded in quantities that exceed 5% of the total prescription orders dispensed or distributed by such pharmacy.
Note: FDA has announced that it is extending the period for states to decide whether to sign the MOU and before FDA begins enforcing the 5% rule. The new deadline for states to sign the MOU and comply with the 5% rule is October 22, 2022.

(4) As of the publication date of this book, Pennsylvania has not entered into an MOU with the FDA addressing inordinate amounts of compounded drugs in interstate commerce. This means beginning October 22, 2022, Pennsylvania pharmacies may not distribute (or cause to be distributed) compounded drug products out of state in quantities that exceed 5% of the total prescription orders dispensed or distributed by such pharmacy.

STUDY TIP: FDA has issued several additional guidance documents to implement the Compounding Quality Act that are beyond the scope of this book. Detailed information may be found on FDA's website.

---

2. Drug Supply Chain Security Act (DSCSA) (Track and Trace).
   a. Provides for a uniform national framework for an electronic track-and-trace system for prescription drugs as they move through the supply chain, and sets national standards for states to license drug wholesaler distributors.
   b. Applies to prescription drugs for human use in finished dosage form, but certain products are exempted, including blood and blood components, radioactive drugs, imaging drugs, certain intravenous products for fluid replacement, dialysis solutions, medical gases, compounded drugs, medical convenience kits containing drugs, certain combination products, sterile water, and products for irrigation.
   c. Manufacturers are required to provide "Transaction Data" for each product sold, wholesalers are required to

receive "Transaction Data" upon purchase and subsequently provide "Transaction Data" to buyers (pharmacies or other wholesalers), and pharmacies are required to receive transaction data and pass this information along if they further distribute the product.

    d. "Transaction Data" includes Transaction Information, Transaction History, and a Transaction Statement.

        (1) Transaction Information includes the product's name, strength, and dosage form; NDC number; container size and number of containers; date of transaction; and name and address of the person from whom ownership is being transferred and to whom ownership is being transferred. A unique product identifier or serialized numerical identifier (SNI) will also be required that identifies an individual bottle or unit of sale.

        (2) Transaction History is a paper or electronic statement that includes prior transaction information for each prior transaction back to the manufacturer.

        (3) Transaction Statement is a paper or electronic statement by the seller that the seller is authorized (licensed), received the product from an authorized (licensed) person, received the transaction information and transaction history from the prior owner if required, did not knowingly ship a suspect or illegitimate product, has systems and processes to comply with verification requirements, and did not knowingly provide false transaction information.

STUDY TIP: Product tracing information, which includes transaction information, history, and statement, must be passed, received, and maintained for 6 years by each supply chain partner.

---

    e. Pharmacies must investigate and properly handle suspect and illegitimate products.

        (1) Suspect products are products that one has reason to believe are potentially counterfeit, diverted, stolen, subject to a fraudulent transaction, or intentionally adulterated, or appear otherwise unfit for distribution such that they would result in serious adverse health consequences or death to humans.

(2) Illegitimate products are products for which credible evidence shows that the products are counterfeit, diverted, stolen, subject of a fraudulent transaction, or intentionally adulterated, or appear otherwise unfit for distribution such that they would result in serious adverse health consequences or death to humans.

(3) Pharmacies must investigate any suspect or illegitimate product. As part of the investigation, a pharmacy must verify the product identifier of at least 3 products or 10% of the suspect product, whichever is greater, or all of the packages if there are fewer than 3. Pharmacies must also verify any illegitimate product in response to a notification of illegitimate product from FDA or a trading partner.
Note: This requirement was scheduled to go into effect on November 27, 2020, but FDA has delayed enforcement until November 27, 2023.

(4) If a product is illegitimate, pharmacies must notify FDA using Form FDA 3911 and notify trading partners within 24 hours. Pharmacies should also work with the manufacturer to prevent an illegitimate product from reaching patients.

f. Pharmacies that are "distributing" (distributing is defined as providing a drug to anyone other than the consumer/patient, as compared to dispensing, which is providing a drug to the patient/consumer) must have a wholesale distribution license and must pass DSCSA transaction data with that distribution. The only exceptions to having a distribution license and passing transaction data are as follows:

(1) When the distribution is between two entities that are affiliated or under common ownership;

(2) When a dispenser is providing product to another dispenser on a patient-specific basis;

(3) When a dispenser is distributing under emergency medical reasons; or

(4) When a dispenser is distributing "minimal quantities" to a licensed practitioner for office use.

g. Other provisions of the DSCSA will be implemented gradually, eventually requiring electronic tracking and tracing of product at the individual package level using a unique product identifier on each package, by 2023.

II. Prohibited Acts Under the FDCA

Nearly all violations of the FDCA cause the products to be adulterated and/or misbranded. It is important to understand the difference between these two concepts. Although drug manufacturers are more likely to violate the FDCA, actions taken by pharmacists (e.g., a dispensing error) could also cause a product to be adulterated or misbranded. It is likely these are the types of situations that may be covered on the MPJE.

A. Adulteration—A drug is adulterated if:

1. It contains any filthy, putrid, or decomposed substance.
2. It has been prepared or held under insanitary conditions where it may have been contaminated.
3. The methods of manufacture do not conform to current good manufacturing practices (cGMPs).
4. It has been manufactured, processed, packed, or held in any factory, warehouse, or establishment and the owner, operator, or agent of such factory, warehouse, or establishment delays, denies, or limits an inspection, or refuses to permit entry or inspection.
5. The container is composed of any poisonous or deleterious substance which may contaminate the drug.
6. It contains an unsafe color additive.
7. It purports to be a drug in an official compendium and its strength differs from or its quality or purity falls below the compendium standard, unless the difference is clearly stated on the label.
   Note: This means that if the product claims to meet USP standards and its strength or quality does not meet those standards, it is adulterated.
8. It is not in a compendium, and its strength differs from or its quality falls below what it represents.
   Note: This means that even if the product does not claim to meet USP standards, if the strength or quality differs or falls below what is stated on its label or labeling, it is adulterated.
9. It is mixed or packed with any substance that reduces its strength or quality, or the drug has been substituted in whole or in part.

B. Misbranding—A drug is misbranded if:
  1. The labeling is false or misleading in any particular way.
  2. It is a prescription drug and the manufacturer's labeling fails to contain the following information:
    a. The name and address of the manufacturer, packer, or distributor.
    b. Brand and/or generic name of the drug or drug product.
    c. The net quantity (weight, quantity, or dosage units).
    d. The weight of active ingredient per dosage unit.
    e. The federal legend "Rx only."
    f. If not taken orally, the specific routes of administration (e.g., for IM injection).
    g. Special storage instructions, if appropriate.
    h. Manufacturer's control number (lot number).
    i. Expiration date.
    j. Adequate information for use. For prescription drugs, this is the package insert and medication guide or patient package insert if required. This also includes other information required (e.g., certain products, including opioids and benzodiazepines, require "black box warnings" to alert healthcare professionals about essential information regarding the product).

STUDY TIP: These labeling requirements are for the manufacturer's container. When a pharmacist dispenses a drug to a patient pursuant to a valid prescription, the label does not have to contain all of these elements. State prescription labeling requirements would dictate what is required on the label.

  3. It is an OTC drug and fails to contain the following:
    a. A principal display panel, including a statement of identity of the product.
    b. The name and address of the manufacturer, packer, or distributor.
    c. Net quantity of contents.
    d. Cautions and warnings needed to protect user.
    e. Adequate directions for safe and effective use (for layperson).

    f. Content and format of OTC product labeling in "Drug Facts" panel format, including:
- **(1)** Active Ingredients.
- **(2)** Purpose.
- **(3)** Use(s)—indications.
- **(4)** Warnings.
- **(5)** Directions.
- **(6)** Other Information.
- **(7)** Inactive Ingredients (in alphabetical order).
- **(8)** Questions? (optional) followed by telephone number.

4. It is a drug liable to deterioration unless it is packaged or labeled accordingly.

5. The container is made, formed, or filled as to be misleading.

6. The drug is an exact imitation of another drug or offered for sale under the name of another drug.

7. It is dangerous to health when used in the dosage or manner suggested in the labeling.

8. It is packaged or labeled in violation of the Poison Prevention Packaging Act.

STUDY TIP: Pharmacists do not usually concern themselves with these labeling requirements as it is expected that manufacturers will label their products appropriately, but you should know the labeling requirements for OTC drugs.

C. Adulteration and Misbranding as Applied to Pharmacies

1. Dispensing a prescription without authorization causes the drug to be misbranded even if it is labeled correctly by the pharmacist. This is because a prescription drug product is only exempt from the manufacturer's labeling requirements in B.2. above when it is dispensed pursuant to a valid prescription.

STUDY TIP: There are a number of drug products that are currently approved and sold for both prescription and OTC use. For example, Prilosec and Prilosec OTC contain the same active ingredient (omeprazole), but the indications for the prescription product require a diagnosis (e.g., GERD) and supervision by a doctor, while the OTC version is indicated for heartburn. Readers should be aware of the common medications that may be sold both as a prescription and OTC, and that their labeling and indications will not be the same. Pharmacists must also have a prescription in order to dispense the prescription product, or the product would be misbranded.

---

2. Misfilling a prescription with the wrong drug, strength, or directions for use will always cause the drug to be misbranded.
3. If a misfilled prescription involves the wrong strength of the drug prescribed, it would also be adulterated. This is because the definition of adulteration includes when the strength differs from or quality falls below that which it represents.
4. If a drug is subject to a Risk Evaluation and Mitigation Strategy (REMS) and it is prescribed or dispensed without meeting the requirements of the REMS, it is misbranded because the REMS program is part of the official labeling of the drug.
5. The advertising or promotion of a compounded drug that is false or misleading would be misbranding.
6. An expired drug product in a manufacturer's bottle is adulterated because after the expiration date, the strength cannot be assured. If a prescription is filled using an expired product, it may also be misbranded if the pharmacist placed a beyond-use date that is after the expiration date of the drug.
7. If the pharmacy counts a medication on a tray that has residue from another medication, the product would be adulterated.
8. If a pharmacy stores inventory in a room or refrigerator where the temperature is not adequately controlled, the products would be adulterated.
9. If the pharmacy stores a specific product incorrectly, such as stocking a medication on a pharmacy shelf instead of in the refrigerator as required, this will lead to the product being adulterated.
10. If a pharmacist fails to dispense a medication in a child-resistant container when required, this would be misbranding.

STUDY TIP: You are more likely to encounter questions related to adulteration and misbranding based on scenarios in a pharmacy.

III. **Other Provisions of the FDCA and Federal Regulations**
   A. Special Warning Requirements for OTC Products in the FDCA

STUDY TIP: These are special labeling requirements under federal regulations for products containing these ingredients. Normally the manufacturer's label would include these warnings, but you should be familiar with these requirements.

1. FD&C Yellow No. 5 (tartrazine) and No. 6 (21 CFR 201.20)—Must disclose presence and provide warning in "precautions" section of label that it may cause allergic reaction in certain susceptible persons.
2. Aspartame (21 CFR 201.21)—Must contain warning in "precautions" section of labeling to the following effect: Phenylketonurics: Contains phenylalanine __ mg per __ (dosage unit).
3. Sulfites (21 CFR 201.22)—Prescription drugs containing sulfites (often used as a preservative) must contain an allergy warning in the "warnings" section of the labeling.
4. Mineral Oil (21 CFR 201.302)—Requires warning to only be taken at bedtime and not be used in infants unless under advice of a physician. Label also cannot encourage use during pregnancy.
5. Wintergreen Oil (methyl salicylate) (21 CFR 201.303 and 201.314(g)(1))—Any drug containing more than 5% methyl salicylate (often used as flavoring agent) must include warning that any use other than directed may be dangerous and that the article should be kept out of reach of children.
6. Sodium Phosphates (21 CFR 201.307)—Limits the amount of sodium phosphates oral solution to not more than 90 ml per OTC container. Also requires specific warnings.
7. Isoproterenol inhalation preparations (21 CFR 201.305)—Requires warning not to exceed dose prescribed and to contact physician if difficulty in breathing persists.
8. Potassium Salt Preparations for Oral Ingestions (21 CFR 201.306)—Requires warning regarding nonspecific small-bowel lesions consisting of stenosis, with or without ulceration, associated with the administration of enteric-coated thiazides with potassium salts.
9. Ipecac Syrup (21 CFR 201.308)
   a. The following statement (boxed and in red letters) must appear: "For emergency use to cause vomiting in poisoning. Before using, call physician, the poison prevention center, or hospital emergency room immediately for advice."
   b. The following warning must appear: "Warning: Keep out of reach of children. Do not use in unconscious persons."

    c. The dosage of the medication must appear. The usual dosage is 1 tablespoon (15 ml) in individuals over 1 year of age.

    d. May only be sold in 1 oz. (30 ml) containers.

10. Phenacetin (acetophenetidin) (21 CFR 201.309)—Must contain warning about possible kidney damage when taken in large amounts or for a long period of time.

11. Salicylates (21 CFR 201.314)—Aspirin and other salicylate drugs must have special warnings for use in children, including warning regarding Reye's syndrome. Retail containers of 11/4 grain (pediatric) aspirin cannot be sold in containers holding more than 36 tablets.

12. OTC Drugs for Minor Sore Throats (21 CFR 201.315)—Any OTC product label that states "For the temporary relief of minor sore throats" must include this warning: "Warning—Severe or persistent sore throat or sore throat accompanied by high fever, headache, nausea, and vomiting may be serious. Consult physician promptly. Do not use more than 2 days or administer to children under 3 years of age unless directed by physician."

13. Alcohol Warning (21 CFR 201.322)—Internal analgesics and antipyretics, including acetaminophen, aspirin, ibuprofen, naproxen, ketoprofen, etc., are required to have a warning for persons consuming 3 or more alcoholic beverages per day and to consult with a doctor before taking.

14. OTC drugs for vaginal contraceptive and spermicide use containing nonoxynol 9 as the active ingredient (21 CFR 201.325)—Are subject to several warning requirements, including "Sexually transmitted diseases (STDs) alert: This product does not protect against HIV/AIDS or other STDs and may increase the risk of getting HIV from an infected partner."

15. OTC Pain Relievers (21 CFR 201.326)

    a. Acetaminophen.

      (1) Must have "acetaminophen" prominently displayed.

      (2) Must warn about liver toxicity.

      (3) Must warn not to use with other products containing acetaminophen and to talk to a doctor or pharmacist before taking with warfarin.

    b. Nonsteroidal Anti-inflammatory Drugs (NSAIDs).

      (1) Must include term "NSAID" prominently on label.

      (2) Must contain "stomach bleeding" warning.

16. OTC Products Containing Iron in Solid Oral Dosage Form (21 CFR 310.518(a))
   a. Must provide the following warning: "Accidental overdose of iron-containing products is a leading cause of fatal poisoning in children under 6. Keep this product out of reach of children. In case of accidental overdose, call a doctor or poison control center immediately."
   b. This warning requirement also applies to dietary supplements containing iron through 21 CFR 101.17(e).
   c. FDA previously had a rule that required unit-dose packaging for iron-containing dietary supplements and drug products that contain 30 milligrams (mg) or more of iron per dosage unit, but that rule was eliminated based on a court case in 2003 that concluded FDA did not have the authority to pass such a rule.

B. Additional OTC Requirements
   1. Tamper-Evident Packaging—Manufacturers and packagers of OTC drugs (except dermatological, dentifrice, insulin, or lozenge products) for sale at retail must package products in a tamper-evident package. OTC products not packaged properly would be considered misbranded and adulterated.
   2. Repackaging of OTC Products—A pharmacist that repackages OTC products would be subject to cGMP requirements and would have to meet all additional requirements, including the manufacturer labeling and tamper-evident packaging, if offered for sale to the public.

STUDY TIP: If a patient wishes to purchase an OTC drug in a smaller package size than what is commercially available, a pharmacist cannot break open a commercial OTC product and sell the lesser quantity by placing it in a vial and labeling it. The only way this can be done is if the patient has a prescription for the smaller quantity and the OTC drug is filled as a prescription, as discussed below.

---

   3. When an OTC product is prescribed and filled as a prescription, the OTC labeling requirements do not have to be followed. The prescription drug labeling requirements would apply and would include the prescriber's directions for use. If an OTC drug is filled as a prescription, any instructions for refills would apply, as would beyond-use dates (valid for one year).

C. FDA Drug and Device Recall Classifications
  1. Class I—Reasonable probability product will cause either serious adverse effects on health or death.
  2. Class II—May cause temporary or medically reversible adverse effects on health or where probability of serious adverse effects is remote.
  3. Class III—Not likely to cause adverse health consequences.
D. Advertising and Promotion of Prescription Drugs
  1. Prescription drug advertising is regulated by FDA.
  2. OTC drug advertising is regulated by the Federal Trade Commission (FTC).
  3. Advertising of Prescription Drug Prices (including by pharmacists)—The advertising of prescription drug prices is considered reminder advertising under FDA regulations (21 CFR 200.200). However, such advertising is exempt from FDA advertising regulations provided that the following conditions are met:
     a. The only purpose of the advertising is to provide information on price, not information on the drug's safety, efficacy, or indications for use.
     b. The advertising contains the proprietary name of the drug (if any), the generic name of the drug, the drug's strength, the dosage form, and the price charged for a specific quantity of the drug.
     c. The advertising may include other information, such as the availability of professional or other types of services, as long as it is not misleading.
     d. The price stated in the advertising shall include all charges to the consumer; mailing and delivery fees, if any, may be stated separately.
     Note: Pennsylvania also prohibits pharmacies from advertising or promoting the sale of controlled substances. See PBOP Rule 49 Pa. Code § 27.18(r)(2)
  4. A pharmacy that compounds products may advertise that they provide compounding services, including that they compound specific products. However, if a pharmacy makes any therapeutic claims regarding those products, they would be subject to FDA's rules on advertising, which are complex and beyond the scope of this book.

E. Patient Package Inserts (PPIs)
   1. Supplied by the manufacturer and written for a layperson.
   2. Required to be given to patients in the outpatient pharmacy setting when new and refill prescriptions for certain products are dispensed.
   3. Currently required for:
      a. Oral contraceptives (21 CFR 310.501).
      b. Estrogen-containing products (21 CFR 310.515).
   4. Hospitalized or institutionalized patients—A PPI must be provided to a patient prior to the first administration of the drug and every 30 days thereafter.

STUDY TIP: Providing PPIs to hospitalized or institutionalized patients probably does not happen in practice, but you need to know that it is technically required.

---

   5. Failure to provide a PPI for these drugs would cause them to be misbranded.
F. Medication Guides (MedGuides)
   1. Similar to PPI program but with amended requirements for institutionalized patients.
   2. FDA requires Medication Guides for all new and refill prescriptions dispensed in the outpatient pharmacy setting when:
      a. Patient labeling could prevent serious adverse effects.
      b. Product has serious risks relative to benefits.
      c. Patient adherence to directions is crucial.
   3. Medication Guides must be written in a standard format and in language suitable for patients.
   4. Manufacturers must obtain FDA approval before distributing Medication Guides and are responsible for ensuring that a sufficient number of Medication Guides are provided to pharmacies. Many manufacturers include the Medication Guide at the bottom of the package insert, but most pharmacy computer systems also print Medication Guides for the products that need them at the time of dispensing.
   5. FDA maintains a searchable Medication Guide database on its website, and there are over 1,000 products that now require a Medication Guide. Some of the drugs, drug classes, and biologicals requiring Medication Guides include:

    a. Accutane® (isotretinoin)
    b. Antidepressants in children and teenagers
    c. Coumadin® (warfarin sodium)
    d. Epogen® (epoetin alfa)
    e. Forteo® (teriparatide, rDNA origin)
    f. Lindane® shampoo and lotion
    g. Lotronex® (alosetron hydrochloride)
    h. Nolvadex® (tamoxifen)
    i. Non-Steroidal Anti-Inflammatory Drugs (NSAIDs)
    j. Remicade® (infliximab)
    k. Trizivar® (abacavir sulfate, lamivudine, and zidovudine)
    l. Opioid analgesics and cough products
    m. Benzodiazepines

6. Failure to provide a Medication Guide when dispensing a drug that requires one would cause the drug to be misbranded.

STUDY TIP: Consumer Medication Information (CMI), which is often provided to community pharmacy patients for all new and refill prescriptions dispensed, is written patient information that is not equivalent to or substitutable for FDA regulated and mandated PPIs and MedGuides.

G. Prescription Drugs: Side Effects Statement

    1. To enable consumers to report side effects of prescription drugs to the FDA, pharmacies and pharmacists are required to distribute a side effects statement to patients when dispensing all new and refill prescriptions in the outpatient setting.

    2. The side effects statement provided with each prescription drug must read "Call your doctor for medical advice about side effects. You may report side effects to FDA at 1-800-FDA-1088."

    3. The side effects statement can be distributed on a sticker attached to the pharmacy container, on a preprinted pharmacy prescription vial cap, on a separate sheet of paper, or found within CMI or MedGuides.

H. Risk Evaluation and Mitigation Strategies (REMS)

    1. REMS are strategies to manage a known or potential serious risk associated with a drug, drug class, or biological product. FDA requires a REMS if FDA finds that it is necessary to ensure that the benefits of the drug, drug class, or biological product outweigh the risks of the product. A REMS can include a Medication Guide, a Patient Package Insert, a communication plan, elements to assure safe use, and an implementation system. It must also include a timetable for assessment of the REMS.

2. Elements to assure safe use may include:
   a. Special training, experience, or certification of health-care practitioners prescribing the drugs;
   b. Special certification for pharmacies, practitioners, or healthcare settings that dispense the drug;
   c. Dispensing drugs to patients only in certain healthcare settings such as hospitals;
   d. Dispensing drugs to patients with evidence or other documentation of safe use conditions, such as laboratory test results;
   e. Monitoring patients using the drug; or
   f. Enrolling each patient using the drug in a registry.

3. A complete list of products with approved REMS can be found on FDA's website and may include an entire drug class, such as the Opioid Analgesic REMS. I have included summaries of two of the most extensive REMS below, but you should be familiar with the most common REMS and which products are subject to a REMS.

STUDY TIP: Some REMS place requirements only on prescribers. You are more likely to be asked questions about REMS programs that place requirements on pharmacists.

---

4. Example REMS—Isotretinoin (Accutane) iPLEDGE Program
   a. Only doctors registered in iPLEDGE can prescribe isotretinoin. Doctors registered with iPLEDGE must agree to assume the responsibility for pregnancy counseling of female patients of childbearing potential. Prescribers must obtain and enter into the iPLEDGE system negative test results for those female patients of childbearing potential prior to prescribing isotretinoin.
   b. Only patients registered in iPLEDGE can be prescribed isotretinoin. In addition to registering with iPLEDGE, patients must comply with a number of key requirements that include completing an informed consent

form, obtaining counseling about the risks and requirements for safe use of the drug, and, for women of childbearing potential, complying with required pregnancy testing and use of contraception.

c. Only pharmacies registered in iPLEDGE can dispense isotretinoin. To register in iPLEDGE, a pharmacy must select a Responsible Site Pharmacist who must obtain iPLEDGE program information and registration materials via the internet (*www.ipledgeprogram.com*) or telephone (1-866-495-0654) and sign and return the completed registration form. To activate registration, the Responsible Site Pharmacist must access the iPLEDGE program via the internet (*www.ipledgeprogram.com*) or telephone (1-866-495-0654) and attest to the following points:

(1) I know the risk and severity of fetal injury/birth defects from isotretinoin.

(2) I will train all pharmacists on the iPLEDGE program requirements.

(3) I will comply and seek to ensure that all pharmacists comply with the iPLEDGE program requirements.

(4) I will obtain isotretinoin from iPLEDGE-registered wholesalers.

(5) I will return to the manufacturer (or delegate) any unused product.

(6) I will not fill isotretinoin for any party other than a qualified patient.

d. To dispense isotretinoin, pharmacists must obtain authorization from iPLEDGE via the internet (*www.ipledgeprogram.com*) or telephone (1-866-495-0654) signifying the patient is registered, has received counseling and education, and is not pregnant.

e. Females of reproductive potential have a 7-day prescription window to get an isotretinoin prescription filled. This 7-day window starts with the pregnancy test specimen collection date, not the date of the result of the test.

f. Product is dispensed in blister packages that cannot be broken, and a 30-day supply is the maximum quantity that can be dispensed.

g. No refills are allowed.

5. Example REMS—Thalomid (thalidomide) REMS

    a. Prescriber Requirements

        (1) The prescriber enrolls and becomes certified with Celgene for the Thalomid REMS program.

        (2) The prescriber counsels patient on benefits and risks of Thalomid.

        (3) The prescriber provides contraception and emergency contraception counseling.

        (4) The prescriber verifies negative pregnancy test for all female patients of reproductive potential.

        (5) The prescriber completes a Thalomid Patient-Physician Agreement Form with each patient and sends to Celgene.

        (6) The prescriber/patient completes applicable mandatory confidential survey.

        (7) The prescriber obtains an authorization number from Celgene and writes it on every prescription along with patient risk category.

        (8) The prescriber writes no more than a 4-week (28-day) supply, with no automatic refills or telephone prescriptions.

        (9) The prescriber sends Thalomid prescription to a certified pharmacy.

    b. Pharmacy Requirements

        (1) Pharmacy must be certified in the Thalomid REMs program with Celgene.

        (2) Prescriptions can only be accepted with an authorization number and patient risk category.

        (3) Authorization numbers are valid for 7 days from the date of the last pregnancy test for females of reproductive potential and 30 days from the date issued for other patients.

        (4) Pharmacy must obtain a confirmation number prior to dispensing via toll-free number or online. The confirmation number is valid for 24 hours and must be entered on the prescription. This means the prescription must be dispensed within 24 hours of obtaining the confirmation number.

        (5) No automatic refills or telephone prescriptions are permitted.

(6) Prescriptions must be written for 4-week (28-day) supply or less.

(7) No refills are allowed and subsequent prescriptions may be dispensed only if there are 7 days or less remaining on the existing prescription.

(8) A certified Thalomid REMS counselor must counsel the patient, and counseling must be documented.

(9) Prescriptions must be dispensed with a medication guide.

(10) Prescriptions cannot be transferred to another pharmacy without prior authorization from Celgene.

I. National Drug Code (NDC) Number

1. A unique 10-character number that identifies a particular drug by manufacturer or packager (labeler), product, and package size. NDC numbers will have one of the following configurations: 4-4-2, 5-3-2, or 5-4-1.

   a. First 4 to 5 digits = labeler code.

   b. Next 3 to 4 digits = specific drug, strength, dosage form.

   c. Last 1 to 2 digits = package size.

2. NDC numbers are required for a drug manufacturer to list its product with FDA, and FDA suggests they be included on the drug's label, although it is not technically required. All drug manufacturers include an NDC number because they facilitate automated processing of drug data by government agencies, third-party payers, wholesalers, and manufacturers.

STUDY TIP: NDC numbers should not appear on non-drug products. If a dietary supplement or medical device has an NDC number on its label, it would be misbranded. Medical devices have unique device identifiers (UDIs) instead of NDC numbers. Any product that implies it is an FDA-approved drug when it is not would also be misbranded.

---

3. While nearly all drug products have an NDC number, an NDC code does not indicate a drug is approved by FDA. There are some unapproved drugs that have NDC numbers.

4. FDA has proposed to standardize the NDC format and move to an 11-digit code, but that proposed change has not yet been adopted. Although the NDC is 10 digits, the standard for billing and claims submissions is an 11-digit NDC. This is accomplished by inserting a leading zero into one of the segments: the first segment if it is four numbers, the second segment if it is three numbers, or added to the beginning of the third segment if it only has one number.

J. FDA Orange Book

1. Official name is *Approved Drug Products with Therapeutic Equivalence Evaluations.*
2. Available at *http://www.fda.gov/cder/ob/.*
3. The primary source for determining generic equivalency of drugs. To be considered generically equivalent, a drug must be both pharmaceutically equivalent and therapeutically equivalent to the reference drug product (normally the brand-name drug).
4. Definitions
   a. Pharmaceutical equivalents are drug products in identical dosage forms and route(s) of administration that contain identical amounts of the identical active drug ingredient.
   b. Therapeutic equivalents are approved drug products that are pharmaceutical equivalents for which bioequivalence has been demonstrated, and they can be expected to have the same clinical effect and safety profile when administered to patients under the conditions specified in the labeling.
   Note: This means the drug is bioequivalent to the reference drug product.
5. Uses 2-letter coding system to indicate equivalency, with first letter being the key:
   a. A = Drug products that the FDA considers to be pharmaceutically equivalent and therapeutically equivalent.
   b. B = Drug products that the FDA considers NOT to be pharmaceutically equivalent and therapeutically equivalent.

STUDY TIP: The first letter of the 2-letter code tells you if the product is considered equivalent. It is recommended that the reader look up an Orange Book listing in the FDA Orange Book database online and be familiar with its format.

---

6. Products with no known or suspected bioequivalence issues:
   a. AA—conventional dosage forms.
   b. AN—solutions and powders for aerosolization.
   c. AO—injectable oil solutions.
   d. AP—injectable aqueous solutions.
   e. AT—topical products.

7. Products with actual or potential bioequivalence problems but for which adequate scientific evidence has established bioequivalence for those products are given a rating of AB.

8. There are situations where there may be multiple pharmaceutically equivalent reference drugs that have not been determined to be bioequivalent to each other. For these products, the FDA implemented a three-character code such as AB1, AB2, and AB3. If a generic drug product establishes bioequivalence to one of the reference drugs, it will receive the same three-character code as the reference drug. An example includes Adalat CC (AB1) and Procardia XL (AB2), which are both reference drugs with the same dosage form and active ingredients, but they are not rated as bioequivalent to one another.

K. FDA Purple Book

1. Official name is *Lists of Licensed Biological Products with Reference Product Exclusivity and Biosimilarity or Interchangeability Evaluations.*

2. Lists biological products that are considered biosimilars and provides interchangeability evaluations for these products.

3. "Biosimilar" or "biosimilarity" means that the biological product is highly similar to the reference product, notwithstanding minor differences in clinically inactive components, and there are no clinically meaningful differences between the biological product and the reference product in terms of the safety, purity, and potency of the product.

4. An "interchangeable product" is a product that has been shown to be biosimilar to the reference product and can be expected to produce the same clinical result as the reference product in any given patient.

5. Only biological products that have been designated "interchangeable" may be substituted for the original reference product by a pharmacist. Biosimilar products would require prescriber intervention in order to substitute.

STUDY TIP: The FDA Orange Book and Purple Book are federal references that guide healthcare professionals in evaluating the substitution of approved drug products and biologics. States may also adopt these references as law; the states that do this are often termed Orange Book and/or Purple Book states. Pennsylvania is an Orange and Purple Book state, meaning pharmacists can substitute

A-rated generic products and interchangeable rated biological products without first contacting the prescriber. However, Pennsylvania excludes from the definition of generic-equivalent drug products those deemed narrow therapeutic index (NTI) drugs. Therefore, in Pennsylvania, pharmacists would not be permitted to automatically substitute a generic product with an A rating if it was considered an NTI drug. *See Pennsylvania Generic Equivalent Drug Law and Regulations Chapter 4, Section IV, for additional information.*

Note: While there are several biosimilar products on the market (such as adalimumab, bevacizumab, and epoetin alfa), as of the date of publication of this book, FDA had only designated one of them as interchangeable. As of July 2021, Semglee (insulin glargine-yfgn) was approved by FDA as interchangeable with (can be substituted at the pharmacy level for) its reference product Lantus (insulin glargine).

L. Medical Devices

1. The FDA regulates companies that manufacturer and repackage medical devices.

2. A medical device includes instruments, apparatuses, machines, implants, or other related articles intended to treat or prevent disease but, unlike drugs, does not achieve its primary purpose through chemical action within or on the body and does not depend on being metabolized.

3. The FDA classifies medical devices based on the risk association with the device.

   a. Class I devices are deemed to be low risk and are therefore subject to the least regulatory controls. Dental floss is an example.

   b. Class II devices are higher risk and require greater regulatory controls. Syringes are an example.

   c. Class III devices are generally the highest risk devices and are subject to the highest level of regulatory control, and those that pose a significant risk of illness or injury require premarket approval by the FDA. Replacement heart valves are an example.

4. Not all medical devices require a prescription, but most do (e.g., contact lenses).

5. Certain Class I and Class II devices are exempt from premarket approval and GMPs, but typically must still comply with other regulatory requirements unless exempt.

M. Animal Drugs
1. The FDA regulates drugs intended to be used by animals.
2. Animal drugs have to be approved by the FDA as safe and effective.
3. The FDA will determine if an animal drug can be sold as a prescription or OTC drug.
4. Animal prescription products can be dispensed only by or upon the lawful written order of a licensed veterinarian.
5. The manufacturer's label of an animal prescription drug product must bear the legend *"Caution: Federal law restricts this drug to use by or on the order of a licensed veterinarian."*
6. Veterinarians can legally prescribe approved human drugs for animals in certain circumstances (this is called extra-label or off-label use). Therefore, pharmacies and pharmacists may receive and dispense such prescriptions.
7. The FDA has released guidance regarding the compounding of animal drugs, which allows pharmacies to compound animal drugs.
8. State laws and professional associations often require or suggest veterinarians to notify an animal owner that certain prescription medications for animals may be available at a pharmacy. The animal owner then has the option of obtaining the medication from the veterinarian or obtaining a prescription for the medication to be filled at a pharmacy of his or her choice.

IV. Poison Prevention Packaging Act of 1970 (PPPA)
A. Administered by Consumer Product Safety Commission (CPSC).
B. Requires child-resistant containers for all prescription drugs and for the following nonprescription drugs, drug classes, preparations, or dietary supplements:
1. Aspirin—Any aspirin-containing preparation for human use in dosage form intended for oral administration.
2. Methyl salicylate (oil of wintergreen)—Liquid preparations containing more than 5% by weight of methyl salicylate unless packaged in pressurized spray containers.
3. Controlled drugs—Any preparation for human use in a dosage form intended for oral administration that consists in whole or in part of any substance subject to control under the Federal Controlled Substances Act.

Note: There are some Schedule V controlled substances available without a prescription under federal law. See Chapter 3

4. Methyl alcohol (methanol)—Household substances in liquid form containing 4% or more by weight of methyl alcohol unless packaged in a pressurized spray container.

5. Iron-containing drugs—With the exception of animal feeds used as vehicles for the administration of drugs, non-injectable animal and human drugs providing iron for therapeutic or prophylactic purposes, which contain a total amount of elemental iron equivalent to 250 mg.

6. Dietary supplements containing iron—With the exception of those preparations in which iron is present solely as a colorant, dietary supplements that contain an equivalent of 250 mg or more of elemental iron in a single package.

7. Acetaminophen—Preparations for human use in a dosage form intended for oral administration and containing more than 1 g of acetaminophen in a single package.
   Exemptions:
   a. Acetaminophen-containing effervescent tablets or granules containing less than 10% acetaminophen with a median lethal dose greater than 5 g/kg of body weight and that release at least 85 ml of carbon dioxide per grain of acetaminophen when placed in water.
   b. Unflavored acetaminophen-containing preparations in powder form, other than those intended for pediatric use, that are packaged in unit doses with no more than 13 grains of acetaminophen per unit dose and that contain no other substance subject to the special packaging requirements.

8. Diphenhydramine HCl—Preparations for human use in oral dosage forms containing more than the equivalent of 66 mg of diphenhydramine base in a single package.

9. Ibuprofen—Preparations for human use in oral dosage forms containing 1 gram or more of ibuprofen in a single package.

10. Loperamide—Preparations for human use in oral dosage forms containing more than 0.045 mg of loperamide in a single package.

11. Lidocaine—Products containing more than 5 mg of lidocaine in a single package (includes all dosage forms, including creams, sprays, and transdermal patches).

12. Dibucaine—Products containing more than 0.5 mg of dibucaine in a single package (includes all dosage forms, including creams, sprays, and transdermal patches).
13. Naproxen—Preparations for human use in oral dosage forms containing 250 mg or more of naproxen in a single package.
14. Ketoprofen—Preparations for human use in oral dosage forms containing more than 50 mg of ketoprofen in a single package.
15. Fluoride—Products containing more than 50 mg of elemental fluoride and more than 0.5% fluoride in a single package.
16. Minoxidil—Preparations for human use containing more than 14 mg of minoxidil in a single package (includes topical products that must continue to meet requirements once applicator is installed by consumer).
17. Imidazolines—Products containing 0.08 mg or more in a single package. Imidazolines are a drug class that includes tetrahydrozoline, naphazoline, oxymetazoline, and xylometazoline and are often found in ophthalmic and nasal products.
18. Any drug switched from Rx to OTC status.
C. Exemptions:
   1. Request of patient or physician.

STUDY TIP: Only the patient can provide a blanket request for all future prescriptions. The prescriber can only request a non-child-resistant container on an individual prescription. The request is not legally required to be in writing, although it is good practice to have it in writing.

---

   2. Bulk containers not intended for household use.
   3. Drugs distributed to institutionalized patients.
   4. One package size of OTC drugs designed for the elderly.
   5. Prescription drugs packaged for residents of LTCFs and other institutional settings if the facility personnel will administer the medications to the patients.
   6. Specific prescription and nonprescription drug exemptions include:
      a. Oral contraceptives, conjugated estrogens, and norethindrone acetate in manufacturer's dispenser package.
      b. Medroxyprogesterone acetate tablets.
      c. Sublingual nitroglycerin and sublingual and chewable isosorbide dinitrate of 10 mg or less.

d. Aspirin and acetaminophen in effervescent tablets or granules.
e. Potassium supplements in unit-dose packaging.
f. Sodium fluoride containing not more than 264 mg of sodium fluoride per package.
g. Anhydrous cholestyramine and colestipol packets.
h. Erythromycin ethylsuccinate granules for oral suspension and oral suspensions in packages containing not more than 8 g of erythromycin.
i. Erythromycin ethylsuccinate tablets in packages containing no more than 16 g of erythromycin.
j. Prednisone tablets containing no more than 105 mg per package.
k. Methylprednisolone tablets containing no more than 84 mg per package.
l. Mebendazole tablets containing no more than 600 mg per package.
m. Betamethasone tablets containing no more than 12.6 mg per package.
n. Preparations in aerosol containers intended for inhalation.
o. Pancrelipase preparations.
p. Sucrose preparations in a solution of glycerol and water.
q. Hormone replacement therapy products that rely solely upon the activity of one or more progestogen or estrogen substances.

STUDY TIP: It is important to know all of the products that are exempt from the Poison Prevention Packaging Act, including details as to strengths and dosage forms.

BONUS STUDY TIP: For pharmacies, the law requires dispensing medications in a new vial/bottle and safety cap with each prescription filled. A pharmacy is permitted to reuse a glass container if a new safety cap is provided with each fill.

EXTRA BONUS STUDY TIP: When a pharmacist does not comply with the PPPA, in addition to violating the PPPA (the CPSC enforces), it is also a misbranding violation of the FDCA (the FDA enforces).

V. Other Federal Laws and Regulations

A. Federal Hazardous Substances Act of 1966

   1. The Consumer Product Safety Commission administers and enforces this Act, which is intended to protect consumers from hazardous and toxic substances.

   2. Requires the label on the immediate package of a hazardous product and any outer wrapping or container that might cover up the label on the package to have the following information in English:

   a. The name and business address of the manufacturer, packer, distributor, or seller;

   b. The common or usual or chemical name of each hazardous ingredient;

   c. The signal word "Danger" for products that are corrosive, extremely flammable, or highly toxic;

   d. The signal word "Caution" or "Warning" for all other hazardous products;

   e. An affirmative statement of the principal hazard or hazards that the product presents (e.g., "Flammable," "Harmful if Swallowed," "Causes Burns," "Vapor Harmful," etc.);

   f. Precautionary statements telling users what they must do or what actions they must avoid to protect themselves;

   g. Where it is appropriate, instructions for first aid treatment if the product injures someone;

   h. The word "Poison" for a product that is highly toxic, in addition to the signal word "Danger";

   i. If a product requires special care in handling or storage, instructions for consumers to follow to protect themselves; and

   j. The statement "Keep out of the reach of children." If a hazardous product such as a plant does not have a package, it still must have a hang tag that contains the required precautionary information. That information must also be printed in any literature that accompanies the product and that contains instructions for use.

   3. The act does not apply to drugs regulated by FDA, but may apply to other products sold in a pharmacy such as bleach, cleaning fluids, antifreeze, etc.

B. Hazard Communication Standard

    1. The Occupational and Safety Health Administration (OSHA) administers and enforces this regulation, which requires employers (including pharmacies) that deal with hazardous materials to meet the Hazard Communication Standard. *See 29 CFR 1910.1200*

    2. The standard requires chemical manufacturers and importers to classify the hazards of chemicals they produce or import and to prepare appropriate labels and Safety Data Sheets (SDS), which were formerly known as Material Safety Data Sheets (MSDS).

    3. Drugs in solid, final dosage form for administration to patients are exempt from these requirements, but hazardous chemicals or products not in solid, final dosage form for administration (such as liquid products used in compounding) may be covered. Generally, a pharmacy may rely on the manufacturer to determine if a product is considered hazardous. If a pharmacy has any such products, they are required to have a written Hazard Communication Plan.

    4. The plan must include a list of hazardous chemicals in the workplace, must ensure all such products are appropriately labeled and have a Safety Data Sheet, and must include training for all workers on the hazards of chemicals, appropriate protective measures, and where and how to obtain additional information.
Note: Additional details can be found in OSHA's publication "Small Entity Compliance Guide for Employers that Use Hazardous Chemicals."

C. Centers for Medicare and Medicaid Services (CMS) Requirements

    1. Tamper-Resistant Prescriptions—CMS requires that all written prescriptions meet certain tamper-resistant requirements to prevent unauthorized copying and to prevent counterfeiting (with some exceptions). The tamper-evident features must include:

        a. One or more industry-recognized features designed to prevent unauthorized copying of a completed or blank prescription form;

        b. One or more industry-recognized features designed to prevent the erasure or modification of information written on the prescription pad by the prescriber; and

    c. One or more industry-recognized features designed to prevent the use of counterfeit prescription forms.

  2. Pharmacy Services at Long Term Care Facilities:

    a. Medication Regimen Reviews—CMS regulations require a consultant pharmacist to perform a Medication Regimen Review for all long-term care patients every 30 days. The pharmacist must report any irregularities to the attending physician, the facility's medical director, and the facility's director of nursing, and these reports must be acted upon.

    b. Each resident's drug therapy must be free from unnecessary drugs. This includes drugs at excessive doses or durations and limiting psychotropic drugs to diagnosed and documented conditions.

    c. When ordered and used as needed (PRN), psychotropic drugs must be limited to 14 days unless the practitioner documents the rationale for extending an order beyond 14 days. PRN orders for psychotropic drugs cannot be renewed unless the attending physician evaluates the resident for the appropriateness of that drug.

    d. To reduce medication waste, pharmacies may not dispense more than a 14-day cycle of medications to LTCF residents, with limited exceptions.

    e. Pharmacies must ensure routine and emergency drugs are provided in a timely manner to all residents. The use of emergency medication kits is permissible to help meet this requirement.

D. Delivering Prescriptions by U.S. Mail or Common Carrier

  1. Delivery by Mail (postal regulations administered by the U.S. Postal Service)—General postal regulations do not allow dangerous substances to be mailed; however, there are exceptions for prescription drugs.

    a. Non-controlled—Prescriptions containing non-controlled substances may be mailed by a pharmacy to the ultimate user, provided that the medications are not alcoholic beverages, poisons, or flammable substances.

    b. Controlled substances may be mailed to patients under the following requirements:

      (1) The prescription container must be labeled in compliance with prescription labeling rules;

(2) The outer wrapper or container in which the prescription is placed must be free of markings that would indicate the nature of the contents (including the name of the pharmacy as part of the return address on the mailing package, as that may alert individuals that drugs may be in the package); and

(3) No markings of any kind may be placed on the package to indicate the nature of the contents.

    c. Controlled substances may be mailed to other DEA registrants (practitioners, other pharmacies, distributors, or drug disposal firms), provided they are placed in a plain outer container or securely overwrapped in plain paper and all recordkeeping requirements are met.

  2. Delivery by Common Carrier—Any prescription drug may be delivered from a pharmacy to a patient by common carrier such as the United Parcel Service (UPS) or FedEx. This includes all schedules of controlled substances and dangerous drugs. Common carriers are not subject to postal regulations.

E. Federal Tax-Free Alcohol Regulations

  1. Pharmacies sometimes use 95% ethanol (190 proof) for compounding purposes.

  2. When used for scientific, medicinal, or mechanical purposes or to treat patients, such alcohol is considered "tax free."

  3. The Alcohol and Tobacco Tax and Trade Bureau (TTB) regulates tax-free alcohol with the federal Bureau of Alcohol, Tobacco, Firearms, and Explosives (ATFE). ATFE is responsible for enforcement.

  4. A user permit must be acquired from TTB and specific recordkeeping requirements must be met.

  5. Tax-free alcohol cannot be resold or used in any beverage product.

VI. Privacy—HIPAA and HITECH (Enforced by the Office of Civil Rights)

A. Most pharmacies are a "covered entity" under HIPAA and must be in compliance with these requirements.

B. Notice and Acknowledgement

  1. Pharmacies must provide patients with a "Notice of Privacy Practices" and make a good faith effort to obtain a written acknowledgement of receipt of the Notice from the patient.

2. The Notice must be provided upon first service delivery to the patient.
3. The HIPAA privacy rule requires mandatory provisions in the Notice.

C. Use and Disclosure of Protected Health Information (PHI)
   1. Protected Health Information (PHI) is the HIPAA term for patient-identifiable information.
   2. Pharmacies may use and disclose PHI to provide treatment for payment and for healthcare operations without authorization from the patient.
   3. Pharmacies may also use and disclose PHI for certain governmental functions without authorization from the patient. This includes uses and disclosures for public health activities such as reporting adverse events to FDA, to health oversight agencies such as boards of pharmacies or state drug monitoring programs, and to law enforcement agencies.
   4. Other uses and disclosures, such as for marketing purposes, require a signed authorization from the patient. If the covered entity receives remuneration for the marketing, the authorization form must expressly inform the patient of such.
   5. Face-to-face communications about alternative drugs or health products are considered part of treatment and not marketing.
   6. Refill reminders for a currently prescribed drug (or one that has lapsed for not more than 90 days) are not considered marketing as long as any payment made to the pharmacy in exchange for making the communication is reasonable and related to the pharmacy's cost of making the communication.
   7. Minimum Necessary Standard
      a. When using and disclosing PHI, a pharmacy must make reasonable efforts to limit PHI to the minimum necessary to accomplish the intended purpose.
      b. The minimum necessary standard does not apply to disclosures to healthcare providers for treatment purposes. These disclosures would include prescription transfers or providing prescription information to physicians.
      c. The minimum necessary standard does not apply to disclosures for which the patient has signed an authorization.

      d. The minimum necessary standard does apply to disclosures for payment.

  8. Incidental Disclosures

      a. Unintended "incidental" disclosures are not a violation of the Privacy Rule as long as reasonable safeguards are in place.

      b. Examples: Sales representatives or janitorial service members accidentally see PHI during the normal course of their jobs; a customer overhears counseling that is performed in a private area in a discreet manner.
Note: PHI must be properly disposed of by pharmacies. There are examples of pharmacies being fined for improperly disposing of PHI (such as labeled pharmacy vials and paper records) into dumpsters accessible to the public and unauthorized individuals.

D. Business Associates (BAs)

  1. BAs are persons or entities, other than members of a pharmacy's workforce, who perform a function or service on behalf of the pharmacy that requires the use or disclosure of PHI.

  2. Pharmacies are required to enter into business associate contracts with these BAs, which require the BAs to meet many of the same requirements for protecting PHI as a covered entity under HIPAA.

E. Patient Rights and Administrative Requirements

  1. Patients have a right to access and obtain a copy of their PHI. Pharmacies must comply with a request within 30 days, but may extend time by no more than 30 additional days if they notify the individual of the reason for the delay.

  2. Patients have a right to amend their PHI records and request an accounting of disclosures of their PHI made by a pharmacy under certain circumstances. Pharmacies must comply with a request to amend or request for an accounting of disclosures within 60 days, but may extend it by no more than 30 additional days if they notify the individual of the reason for the delay.

  3. Pharmacies must establish policies and procedures to protect from accidental or intentional uses and disclosures of PHI through the use of appropriate administrative, technical, and physical safeguards to protect the privacy of PHI.

4. Pharmacies must train all employees on privacy policies and impose sanctions on employees for any violations of privacy policies.

5. Pharmacies must designate a Privacy Official who is responsible for development and implementation of HIPAA-related policies, procedures, and compliance.

6. Pharmacies must also designate a contact person to receive complaints. This person may also be the Privacy Official.

F. HITECH Act—The HITECH Act amended HIPAA to strengthen many of its provisions. Among other things, the HITECH Act added a breach notification requirement that requires:

1. Covered Entities, including pharmacies, to notify individuals of a breach of their "unsecured" PHI within 60 calendar days after the breach is discovered.

2. BAs must report any breaches of unsecured PHI to the covered entity and provide the identities of each affected individual.

3. A "breach" is defined as unauthorized acquisition, access, use, or disclosure of PHI that compromises its security or privacy. It does not include instances in which there has been an inadvertent disclosure from an authorized individual to another person authorized to access PHI within the same organization. A breach also does not include instances in which the covered entity or BA has a good faith belief that the PHI is not further acquired, accessed, retained, used, or disclosed.

4. For breaches affecting fewer than 500 individuals, covered entities must maintain a log of these breaches and notify HHS of these breaches annually.

5. If more than 500 individuals are affected, the Secretary of HHS and prominent local media must be notified in addition to the affected individuals within 60 days after the breach is discovered.

CHAPTER TWO
Federal Controlled Substances Act (FCSA) and Pennsylvania Controlled Substance Drug Device and Cosmetic Act (PCSDDCA) and Applicable Rules

CHAPTER TWO

Federal Controlled Substances Act (FCSA) and Pennsylvania Controlled Substance Drug Device and Cosmetic Act (PCSDDCA) and Applicable Rules

Note: Throughout this chapter, unless otherwise noted, requirements listed as part of the FCSA are the same under the PCSDDCA and PCSDDCR. The PCSDDCA and applicable rules incorporate sections very similar to the FDCA and the FCSA, as well as additional state-specific matters such as generic dispensing requirements.

I. Drug Classification

    A. Schedule I (C-I) Drugs

        1. High potential for abuse and severe potential for dependence (addiction).

        2. No currently accepted medical use in treatment in the U.S.

        3. Lack of accepted information on the safety of their use under medical supervision.

        4. Include opiates and derivatives such as heroin and dihydromorphine; hallucinogens such as marijuana, lysergic acid diethylamide (LSD), peyote, and mescaline; and depressants such as methaqualone.

        5. Marijuana is still a Schedule I controlled substance under federal law, although many states have passed laws permitting medical marijuana and, in some cases, recreational marijuana. The general rule is the stricter law always applies, and since marijuana is still illegal under federal law, that should be the applicable law. In reality, the federal government is not interfering with state laws related to marijuana. Because the MPJE competencies include a reference to medical marijuana, one should be familiar with any requirements for dispensing medical marijuana that require pharmacist involvement or licensure from the Board of Pharmacy. Some of the main Pennsylvania requirements relative to medical marijuana are summarized below.

            a. The Pennsylvania Medical Marijuana Program is overseen by the Pennsylvania Department of Health. The Department of Health has temporary regulations implementing the program. Additional information regarding the program can be found on the Pennsylvania Department of Health website and from the temporary regulations. *See 28 Pa. Code §§ 1411 and 1611*

b. The Department of Health issues permits to marijuana dispensaries. A dispensary must obtain this permit before dispensing medical marijuana.

c. To obtain a permit, a dispensary must pay the required fees and provide information that includes describing its business organization and activities and its ability to maintain effective security and control to prevent diversion, abuse, or other illegal conduct.

d. Dispensaries can only employ individuals 18 years of age or older, and no one under the age of 18 can enter the facility unless they are a patient accompanied by a parent.

e. Certified eligible patients must obtain a valid identification card from the Department of Health to have medical marijuana dispensed to them by an approved facility. Physicians are qualified by the state and registered to certify patients with approved medical conditions. Prior to certifying or recertifying a patient, the physician is required to access the state Prescription Drug Monitoring Program (PDMP).

f. Dispensaries must employ a physician, pharmacist, physician assistant (PA), or certified registered nurse practitioner (CRNP). The physician, pharmacist, PA, or CRNP is also required to complete an approved training.

g. The provider dispensing the marijuana must review the patient requirements in the system and follow the prescriber's recommendations regarding the form and dosage. If not provided, the provider is to consult the patient and/or prescriber. The dispensary must enter the form and dosage dispensed into the system.

h. The state will approve which products, forms, and levels of THC can be dispensed by the dispensary. Approved products can only be purchased through state-approved facilities.

i. Dispensaries are restricted in advertising marijuana products and providing promotions.

j. Dispensaries must label the dispensed products with specific information including the grower/processor, name and address of the dispensary, percent of THC and CBD in the product, number of doses, beyond-use date or expiration date, packaging date, and state-required warnings and safety information.

k. The dispensary must maintain inventory data on products received and dispensed and complete a monthly inventory review and annual comprehensive inventory.

STUDY TIP: While Pennsylvania and many other states have "legalized" the medical or recreational use of marijuana, it is still a Schedule I controlled substance under federal law and is technically illegal. Since the stricter law applies, for purposes of the MPJE it is recommended that you treat marijuana as a Schedule I controlled substance unless the question is clearly asking about requirements under state law.

B. Schedule II (C-II) Drugs
1. High potential for abuse.
2. Have a currently accepted medical use in treatment in the U.S. or a currently accepted medical use with severe restrictions.
3. Abuse of the drug or other substances may lead to severe physical or psychological dependence (addiction).
4. Include opium and other narcotics such as morphine, codeine, dihydrocodeine, oxycodone, acetaminophen with hydrocodone (Vicodin®), methadone, meperidine, hydromorphone, fentanyl, and cocaine; stimulants such as amphetamine, methamphetamine, phenmetrazine, and methylphenidate; and depressants such as pentobarbital, secobarbital, amobarbital, glutethimide, and phencyclidine.

STUDY TIP: The term "narcotic" refers to drugs that are derivatives of opium, poppy straw, cocaine, or ecgonine. While all narcotics are controlled substances, not all controlled substances are narcotics.

C. Schedule III (C-III) Drugs
1. Potential for abuse less than Schedule I or II.
2. Have a currently accepted medical use in treatment in the U.S.
3. Abuse of the drug or other substance may lead to moderate or low physical dependence (addiction) or high psychological dependence (addiction).

4. Include some narcotic Schedule II drugs, but in combination with another ingredient, such as aspirin with codeine or acetaminophen with codeine (e.g., Tylenol #3). Also include some non-narcotic drugs, including suppository forms of amobarbital, secobarbital, or pentobarbital; stimulants such as chlorphentermine, phendimetrazine, and benzphetamine; anabolic steroids including testosterone; ketamine; paregoric; Fiorinal®, a combination of butalbital, aspirin, and caffeine; and Fioricet®, a combination of butalbital, acetaminophen, and caffeine.

Note: While Fiorinal® is a Schedule III controlled substance at the federal level, Fioricet® is an exempted prescription drug product (see F. below) and is not labeled as a controlled substance under federal law. Some states, including Pennsylvania, do schedule Fioricet® as a controlled substance.

STUDY TIP: The suppository forms of amobarbital, secobarbital, and pentobarbital are Schedule III, but other dosage forms are Schedule II.

D. Schedule IV (C-IV) Drugs
1. Low potential for abuse relative to Schedule III.
2. Have currently accepted medical use in treatment in the U.S.
3. Abuse may lead to limited physical or psychological dependence (addiction) relative to Schedule III.
4. Include narcotics such as dextropropoxyphene and products with not more than 1 mg of difenoxin and not less than 25 mcgs of atropine sulfate per dosage unit; depressants such as alprazolam, chloral hydrate, diazepam, lorazepam, and phenobarbital; stimulants such as diethylpropion and phentermine; and other drugs such as carisoprodol, tramadol, pentazocine, and butorphanol.

STUDY TIP: Be careful with drugs that have similar names but are in different schedules, such as phenmetrazine (C-II), phendimetrazine (C-III), and phentermine (C-IV).

E. Schedule V (C-V) Drugs
1. Low potential for abuse relative to Schedule IV.
2. Have currently accepted medical use in treatment in the U.S.

3. Abuse of the drug or other substance may lead to limited physical or psychological dependence (addiction) relative to Schedule IV.
4. Include pregabalin (Lyrica®), antitussive products containing codeine, antidiarrheal products containing opium, diphenoxylate and atropine (Lomotil®), and certain anti-seizure drugs such as brivaracetam (Brivact®) and lacosamide (Vimpat®).

STUDY TIP: The 2018 Farm Bill made hemp and hemp derivatives, including cannabidiol (CBD), containing no more than 0.3% tetrahydrocannabinol (THC) non-controlled substances. However, FDA-approved cannabidiol derived from cannabis containing no more than 0.1% THC, such as Epidiolex®, were originally placed into Schedule V. In 2020, DEA removed these products from Schedule V, so they are no longer controlled substances.

F. Exempted Prescription Drug Products
    1. Manufacturers may apply to the DEA to exempt a product or chemical from certain provisions of the Controlled Substances Act (labeling and inventory) if the product or chemical is not likely to be abused. These products may still be considered controlled substances for certain criminal violations even though they are not labeled as controlled substances.
    2. Exempted prescription drug preparations include non-narcotic products containing small amounts of phenobarbital, butalbital, chlordiazepoxide, or meprobamate. A common example is Fioricet® (butalbital, acetaminophen, and caffeine). However, PCSDDCRs schedule barbiturates and barbiturate derivatives as Schedule III; therefore, since Fioricet® contains a barbiturate, it is considered a Schedule III drug in Pennsylvania.
    3. The DEA Exempt Prescription Product List can be found on the DEA's website.
G. Listed Chemicals
    1. Listed Chemicals are chemicals that, in addition to legitimate uses, are used in manufacturing a controlled substance.
    2. In addition to specific chemicals, OTC products containing ephedrine, pseudoephedrine, or phenylpropanolamine are considered Listed Chemicals.
        Note: Ephedrine and phenylpropanolamine products have been removed from the market by FDA for safety reasons.

3. These products are not controlled substances under federal law but are subject to certain sales limitations and other restrictions. *See Section IX.D. below*
  H. Scheduling of Controlled Substances
    1. Federal—U.S. Attorney General, as head of the Department of Justice (which DEA is under), may add, delete, or reschedule substances but must obtain a scientific and medical recommendation from FDA.
    2. State—The Pennsylvania Secretary of Health may add, delete, or reschedule substances by rule under the PCSDDCA.

II. Scheduling of Compounded Controlled Substances
  A. A pharmacy may compound narcotic controlled substances pursuant to a prescription as long as the concentration is not greater than 20%. This 20% concentration limit applies to aqueous or oleaginous solutions or solid oral dosage forms. *See chart of coincident activities allowed at 21 CFR 1301.13.* DEA may consider compounding a narcotic prescription greater than 20% to be manufacturing, which would require the pharmacy to be registered with DEA as a manufacturer.
  B. The narcotic substance must be compounded with one or more non-narcotic therapeutic ingredients.

STUDY TIP: You should know the concentration limits for these narcotics and be able to calculate what schedule a particular compounded product would fall into. However, first be sure that the narcotic is being compounded with another non-narcotic therapeutic agent. Any prescription for a narcotic that is not mixed with another drug, regardless of concentration, will always be in Schedule II. For example, if codeine or opium is only being mixed with water or simple syrup, it is still a Schedule II, regardless of the concentration.

  C. Concentration limits
    1. Codeine
      a. C-V limit = 200 mg/100 ml
      b. C-III limit = 1.8 g/100 ml and 90 mg/dosage unit
        Note: Anything above this limit would be Schedule II.

STUDY TIP: Products such as Cheracol® and Robitussin AC® contain the maximum amount of codeine allowed for Schedule V. If you add any amount of codeine to these products, they would then be Schedule III.

---

2. Dihydrocodeine
   a. C-V limit = 100 mg/100 ml
   b. C-III limit = 1.8 g/100 ml and 90 mg/dosage unit
   Note: Anything above this limit would be Schedule II.
3. Opium
   a. C-V limit = 100 mg/100 ml
   b. C-III limit = 500 mg/100 ml and 25 mg/dosage unit
4. Morphine
   a. C-V limit = None (no morphine products are C-V; they are either C-II or C-III)
   b. C-III limit = 50 mg/100 ml

STUDY TIP: A compounded narcotic prescription will never be a Schedule IV.

III. Registration
A. General Information
   1. Every person or firm that manufactures, distributes, or dispenses any controlled substances or proposes to engage in any of these activities must register with DEA.
   2. There is no state-controlled substance registration requirements for Pennsylvania pharmacies licensed by the PBOP engaged solely in the practice of pharmacy. However, there are requirements for other businesses, such as manufacturers and distributors, to register with the Pennsylvania Department of Health and/or under the Pennsylvania Wholesale Prescription Drug Distributors Licensure Act.
   3. Dispensers (pharmacies and practitioners) register every 3 years with DEA.
   4. Registration form for dispensers, including pharmacies, is DEA Form 224. Renewal form for dispensers is DEA Form 224a. (Online registration is available on the DEA website.)
   5. Registration for dispensers is valid for 3 years.
   6. Dispenser registrations start with the letters "A," "B," or "F" (or "G" for Department of Defense contractors).
   7. The second letter of the prefix will normally be the first letter of the practitioner's last name for individual practitioners or the first letter of a pharmacy's or hospital's name.
B. Mid-Level Practitioners
   1. Registration begins with the letter "M."
   2. May include advanced practice registered nurses and physician assistants if the state allows them to prescribe controlled

substances. Other mid-level practitioners may include optometrists, ambulance services, animal shelters, and veterinary euthanasia technicians. Limited states may include pharmacists as mid-level practitioners.

Note: Pennsylvania does not currently consider pharmacists to be mid-level practitioners.

C. Activities Requiring Separate Registrations
1. Manufacturing (C-I–C-V)
2. Distributing (C-I–C-V)
3. Reverse Distributing (C-I–C-V)
4. Dispensing (C-II–C-V)—Includes prescribing and administration by practitioners and dispensing by pharmacies
5. Conducting research (C-I)
6. Conducting research (C-II–C-V)
7. Conducting narcotic treatment program (C-II–C-V)
8. Conducting chemical analysis (C-I–C-V)
9. Importing (C-I–C-V)
10. Exporting (C-I–C-V)

Note: On October 5, 2020, DEA issued a notice of proposed rulemaking that includes a new category of registration for an Emergency Medical Services Agency. At the time of publication of this book, this proposed rule had not been finalized.

D. Verifying a DEA Registration (number)
1. Step 1—Add 1st, 3rd, and 5th digits.
2. Step 2—Add 2nd, 4th, and 6th digits and multiply sum by 2.
3. Step 3—Add the sum of steps 1 and 2, and the last digit of the sum should correspond to the last digit of the DEA number.
4. Example: DEA #AB1234563.
   a. $1 + 3 + 5 = 9$.
   b. $(2 + 4 + 6) \times 2 = 24$.
   c. Total $= 33$.

E. Separate registration is required for separate locations.
1. Each pharmacy must have a separate DEA registration.
2. DEA will sometimes issue a campus registration that may include multiple buildings for large hospitals or healthcare facilities, but this is done on a case-by-case basis.
3. Individual practitioners, including physicians who register at one location but practice at other locations in the same state, are not required to register at those other locations if they only prescribe controlled substances at those other locations. If a practitioner maintains a supply of controlled substances

at a second site or if the second site is in another state, he or she would have to have an additional DEA registration for that site.

F. Application for Registration

    1. DEA Form 224 for dispensers (practitioners and pharmacies).

    2. Application must be signed (or electronically signed) by the applicant if for an individual, by a partner if it is for a partnership, or by an officer if it is for a corporation.

    3. An applicant can authorize another individual to sign the application and renewals by filling out a Power of Attorney granting that individual the authority and filing that Power of Attorney with the DEA Registration Unit.

    Note: This may be needed if a company (a hospital corporation or a pharmacy corporation) wishes to have a pharmacist be responsible for applying and renewing the DEA registration but the pharmacist is not an officer of the corporation. Unlike the Power of Attorney to sign DEA Form 222, this Power of Attorney must be filed with DEA. See Section IV. A.7. below

G. Exemptions (i.e., who does not have to register with DEA)

    1. An agent or employee of any registered manufacturer, distributor, or dispenser if acting in the usual course of business or employment.

STUDY TIP: Exempted persons would include pharmacists working in a pharmacy and nurses working in a hospital or physician's office.

---

    2. A common or contract carrier or warehouseman or an employee thereof whose possession is in the usual course of business or employment.

    3. An ultimate user (patient) who possesses such substance for a lawful purpose.

    4. Officials of the U.S. Armed Services, Public Health Service, or Bureau of Prisons acting in the course of their official duties.

    Note: Military and federal practitioners are exempt from having to register with DEA, and a pharmacy outside the federal facility may legally fill a prescription issued by such a practitioner. In practice, this is difficult because many pharmacy computer systems will not allow a controlled substance to be filled without a valid prescriber's DEA number, and reporting to prescription monitoring programs may not work without a DEA number. For this reason, many federal practitioners choose to obtain a DEA registration.

H. Practitioner's Use of Hospital DEA Number

    1. Interns, residents, staff physicians, and mid-level practitioners who are agents or employees of a hospital or other institution may administer, dispense, or prescribe controlled substances under the registration of the hospital or other institution when acting in the usual course of business or employment.

    2. The hospital must assign a specific internal code for each practitioner authorized to use the hospital's DEA number, and this must be available at all times to other registrants and law enforcement agencies. This internal code shall be a suffix to the hospital's DEA number (e.g., AP1234563-10 or AP1234563-A12).

    3. Controlled substance prescriptions written by these practitioners are valid and can be filled by any pharmacy, not just the hospital pharmacy where they are employed.

I. Temporary Use of Registration Upon Sale of a Pharmacy

When selling a pharmacy, if the new owner has not yet obtained a DEA registration, DEA permits the new owner to continue the business of the pharmacy under the previous owner's registration, provided the following requirements are met:

    1. The new owner must expeditiously apply for an appropriate DEA registration and state licensure.

    2. The previous owner grants a Power of Attorney to the new owner that provides for the following:

        a. The previous owner agrees to allow the controlled substance activities of the pharmacy to be carried out under his or her DEA registration;

        b. The previous owner agrees to allow the new owner to carry out the controlled substance activities of the pharmacy, including the ordering of controlled substances, as an agent of the previous owner;

        c. The previous owner acknowledges, as the registrant, that he or she will be held accountable for any violations of controlled substance laws that may occur; and

        d. The previous owner agrees that the controlled substance activities of the pharmacy may be carried out under his or her DEA registration and shall remain in effect for no more than 45 days after the purchase date.

IV. Ordering and Transferring Controlled Substances

A. Ordering Schedule II Controlled Substances—DEA Form 222

1. Required for each sale or transfer of C-II drugs (except dispensing to ultimate user).
2. Only one item may be ordered on each numbered line.
3. Orders for etorphine hydrochloride and diprenorphine must contain only orders for these substances.
4. The number of lines completed must be noted on the form.
5. Name and address of supplier from whom the controlled substances are being ordered must be entered.
6. Must be signed (or electronically signed) by the registrant (individual, partner, or officer) or by the person authorized to execute DEA Form 222. *See 7. below*
7. Registrant may authorize other individuals to execute forms by creating a Power of Attorney (POA). This Power of Attorney does not need to be sent to DEA but must be maintained in the pharmacy. A POA must be signed by the person granting the power, the person receiving the power (called the attorney-in-fact), and two witnesses. A sample DEA Power of Attorney can be found in the DEA's Pharmacist Manual and at 21 CFR 1305.05(c).

8. Forms that are not complete, legible, properly prepared, or signed will not be accepted.
9. Forms that show any alteration, erasure, or changes will not be accepted.
10. A supplier may provide a partial quantity for the requested amount, but the remaining quantity must be sent within 60 days or the order becomes void. With the exception of certain Department of Defense orders, no DEA Form 222 is valid more than 60 days after its execution by the purchaser.
11. If a completed order form is lost or stolen, purchaser must prepare another DEA Form 222 along with a statement containing the serial number and date of the lost form and stating that the goods covered by the first order were not received because the form was lost.
12. A pharmacy may fax a completed DEA Form 222 to a supplier in order for the supplier to prepare the order; however, the supplier may not ship the product until the original DEA Form 222 is received and verified.
13. Single Copy DEA Form 222
    a. Effective October 30, 2019, DEA finalized new rules to transition from a triplicate (3 copy) DEA Form 222 to a single copy DEA Form 222 with additional security features. The last date a triplicate DEA Form 222 could be used was October 30, 2021.
    b. The single forms contain 20 order lines per form rather than 10 order lines on the triplicate forms.
    c. The purchaser filling out a single copy DEA Form 222 must make a copy of the original form for its records and submit the original form to the supplier. The copy may be retained in paper or electronic form.
    Note: If kept electronically, the copy of DEA Form 222 does not need to be stored on a different server or system from the purchaser's other records. Also, electronic copies of DEA Form 222 may also be stored on a system at a location different from the registered location. However, the forms must be readily retrievable at all times at the registered location.
    d. The supplier may only fill an order from the original form and not from a copy. The supplier must record on

the original form the number of containers furnished for each ordered item and the date the products are shipped to the purchaser.

Note: There was some confusion as to whether the purchaser or the supplier had to fill out the DEA number of the supplier on the single copy form because the instructions for that part of the form state it is to be entered by the purchaser. This was different from the previous triplicate DEA Form 222, which required the supplier to fill out that section. DEA later clarified that the purchaser should enter that information, but if it is omitted, the supplier may complete that part of the form. See 86 Fed. Reg. 38230 (July 20, 2021)

e. Most suppliers (e.g., wholesalers) are required to report the acquisition and disposition of Schedule II and certain Schedule III and IV controlled substances to DEA's Automation of Reports and Consolidated Orders System (ARCOS). A supplier who reports transactions to ARCOS is not required to send a copy of the original DEA Form 222 to DEA because this information is already reported to ARCOS. However, if a supplier is not required to report transactions to ARCOS (e.g., a pharmacy or practitioner acting as a supplier under the 5% rule), they must submit a copy of the original DEA Form 222 to DEA either by mail or by email to DEA.Orderforms@usdoj.gov when acting as a supplier.

Note: When a pharmacy acts as a supplier, in addition to submitting a copy of DEA Form 222 to DEA by mail or email, it must have a system to flag any suspicious orders, which when identified must be reported online through DEA's Suspicious Orders Report System (SORS).

f. When the product has been received, the purchaser must record the number of containers received and the date received for each item on the copy of the DEA Form 222 they made when ordering the product.

STUDY TIP: The purchaser, or the party obtaining the product, always provides the original DEA Form 222 to the supplier and makes a copy for their records to document products received.

14. Electronic Ordering of Schedule II Controlled Substances
   a. DEA allows electronic ordering of Schedule II controlled substances through the Controlled Substances Ordering System (CSOS).
   b. Each pharmacy must appoint a CSOS coordinator, who will serve as that pharmacy's recognized agent, regarding issues pertaining to issuance of, revocation of, and changes to digital certificates issued under that registrant's DEA registration.
   c. It allows electronic orders based on digital certificates issued by the DEA Certification Authority that are valid until the expiration of the DEA registration for the facility (3 years).
   d. Even though all CSOS Certificates expire when the DEA registration of the facility expires, they are issued to individual subscribers. Certificates must never be used by anyone other than the individual subscriber (a person, not a location) the certificate was issued to.
   e. There are two types of CSOS Certificates:
      (1) CSOS Administrative Certificates are used to digitally sign communications with DEA as well as with other participants in the CSOS community. Administrative Certificates are issued only to CSOS Coordinators and are not valid for electronic ordering.
      (2) CSOS Signing Certificates are used for digitally signing controlled substance orders. Signing Certificates are issued to approved Registrant and Power of Attorney applicants. Approved Coordinator applicants will only be issued a Signing Certificate if he/she holds a valid Power of Attorney for controlled substance ordering and has requested a Signing certificate on his/her CSOS Certificate Application.
   f. All CSOS applications must be audited by an independent third-party auditor prior to use and whenever changes are made to the software to ensure that the software is in compliance with DEA regulations.
   g. An electronic order for controlled substances may not be filled if any of the following occurs:
      (1) The required data fields have not been completed.
      (2) The order is not signed using a digital certificate issued by DEA.

(3) The digital certificate used has expired or been revoked prior to signature.

(4) The purchaser's public key will not validate the digital certificate.

(5) The validation of the order shows that the order is invalid for any reason.

    h. If an order cannot be filled, the supplier must notify the purchaser and provide a statement as to the reason (e.g., improperly prepared or altered). A supplier may, for any reason, refuse to accept any order. If a supplier refuses, a statement that the order is not accepted is sufficient.

    i. When a purchaser receives an unaccepted electronic order from the supplier, the purchaser must electronically link the statement of nonacceptance to the original order. The original statement must be retained for two years. Neither a purchaser nor a supplier may correct a defective order. The purchaser must issue a new order for the order to be filled.

    Note: For details on CSOS, see DEA's e-commerce website at https://www.deaecom.gov/csosmain.html.

B. Ordering Schedule III–V Controlled Substances

    1. Schedule III–V controlled substances can be ordered through normal ordering processes from a wholesaler or manufacturer, but must be documented by a pharmacy with an invoice provided by the wholesaler or manufacturer.

    2. The invoice must contain:

        a. Name of controlled substance.

        b. Dosage form and strength.

        c. Number of units per container (e.g., 100-tablet bottle).

        d. Quantity received (containers).

        e. Date of receipt.

        f. Name, address, and DEA number of the registrant from which the controlled substance was received.

STUDY TIP: It is recommended that you memorize the required elements on an invoice for controlled substances.

C. Transfers of Controlled Substances between Registrants—The 5% Rule

    1. A pharmacy does not have to register with DEA as a distributor as long as total quantities of controlled substances distributed during a 12-month period in which the pharmacy is registered do not exceed 5% of the total quantity of all controlled substances dispensed and distributed during that same 12-month period.

2. Example: A pharmacy dispenses and distributes a total of 10,000 doses (e.g., tablets, capsules, teaspoons) of all controlled substances (not just C-II drugs). This pharmacy would be allowed to transfer 500 doses without being registered with DEA as a distributor.

3. If the transfer is for a Schedule II controlled substance, DEA Form 222 is required. For Schedule III–V controlled substances, an invoice provided by the supplier (i.e., the pharmacy) is required with all of the required elements as listed in B.2. above.

4. Transfers can only be made to the address listed on a DEA registration. This applies to all controlled substances, not just Schedule II controlled substances.

STUDY TIP: Notice that for Schedule II controlled substances, the person receiving the product initiates and fills out DEA Form 222, which is sent to the supplier or seller. However, for Schedule III–V controlled substances, the invoice is provided by the supplier or seller to the purchaser.

V. Additional Requirements for Controlled Substances

A. Storage and Security

1. Pharmacies may store controlled substances in a secure cabinet that is locked.

2. Pharmacies may store controlled substances by dispersal throughout the non-controlled stock to deter theft.

3. Pharmacies may not store all controlled substances on one unsecured shelf.

STUDY TIP: While many pharmacies keep some or all of their controlled substances in locked storage, this is not a legal requirement.

B. Theft or Significant Loss—DEA Form 106

1. A theft or significant loss of controlled substances must be reported in writing to DEA within one business day of discovery of the theft or significant loss. DEA also recommends notifying local police.

2. State or local law enforcement, or Boards of Pharmacy, may also require or suggest notification of a theft or significant loss of controlled substances.

3. Complete DEA Form 106 (Theft or Loss of Controlled Substances). This form can be filled out online at DEA's website.

4. Submitting DEA Form 106 immediately is not necessary if the pharmacy needs time to investigate the facts, but an initial notification must be provided in writing to DEA within one business day of discovery. If the investigation lasts longer than two months, the pharmacy needs to provide an update to DEA.

   Note: At the time of publication of this book, DEA had proposed revising this rule to require that DEA Form 106 be filed within 15 days of discovery. It would also require the form to be filled out online, which almost everyone already does. You should check to see if this rule was adopted as proposed or modified, although it is unlikely to be on the MPJE if it was only recently adopted.

C. Reporting Losses of Listed Chemicals (primarily pseudoephedrine products in a pharmacy)

   1. DEA requires any unusual or excessive loss or disappearance (this would include a theft) of a listed chemical to be reported to DEA at the earliest practicable opportunity.

   2. A written report must be provided within 15 days and must include a description of the circumstances of the loss (in-transit, theft from premises, etc.).

D. Miscellaneous DEA Rules and Policies

   1. Convicted Felon Rule—A pharmacy cannot employ someone who has access to controlled substances if the person has been convicted of a felony involving controlled substances unless a waiver is granted by DEA.

   2. Employee Screening Procedures—DEA requires pharmacies to screen potential employees with specific questions regarding criminal history and use of controlled substances.

   3. Employee Responsibility to Report Drug Diversion—Individual employees are required to report any diversion by other employees to a responsible security official of the employer.

4. Hospital Patient's Possession of Controlled Substances
   a. When a patient is admitted to a hospital via ambulance and no family is present with them, and if the patient has in their possession a legal controlled substance that is medically appropriate for the patient to continue taking, the hospital could secure the medication with the patient's belongings in the patient's hospital room (e.g., in a secured lockbox). Following this guidance avoids the hospital from taking unlawful possession of the controlled substance.
   b. When the patient is admitted with no family present and it has been determined inappropriate for the patient to continue taking the medication(s), or if the hospital has a policy against it, then the hospital has the following options:
      (1) If a family member arrives at the hospital, the medications can be turned over to him or her to take the medications back to the house and/or dispose of them. Or, if the hospital has mail-back packages, these can be provided for the family member and then sealed to mail to a DEA registered reverse distributor for disposal. Lastly, if the hospital is an authorized collector, the family member can dispose of them in the hospital's collection receptacle.
      (2) If no family member arrives, the medications are considered abandoned and the hospital should contact local law enforcement or the local DEA office for guidance. Alternatively, if the state has a law addressing this matter, that law can be followed.
5. Federal Transfer Warning (21 CFR 209.5)—The following warning is required to be on the label of Schedule II–IV controlled substances when dispensed to a patient: "Caution: Federal law prohibits the transfer of this drug to any person other than the patient for whom it was prescribed." The only exception would be for a controlled substance dispensed in a "blinded" clinical study.

STUDY TIP: Federal law requires the transfer warning only for Schedule II–IV controlled substances (not Schedule V). However, Pennsylvania requires it for all controlled substance prescriptions, including Schedule V products. *See PBOP Rule 49 Pa. Code § 27.18(d)(7).* Pharmacies generally comply with this requirement by including this language in small print on every prescription label, but it is legally only required for controlled substances.

E. Disposal and Destruction of Controlled Substance Inventory (drugs not yet dispensed)

   1. On-site destruction of controlled substances in a pharmacy:

      a. Must be done using DEA Form 41, which requires the name and NDC number of the drug and the strength, dosage form, package size, and quantity of the controlled substances destroyed. It also requires recording the method by which the drugs were destroyed and two signatures of employees who witnessed the destruction.

      Note: DEA Form 41 is also used to document destruction of controlled substances that a pharmacy received as an authorized collector even though these drugs are not stock controlled substances because they are not part of the pharmacy's inventory. See F.1. below. DEA Form 41 is also to be used to document non-recoverable breakage or spillage. DEA recommends that two individuals sign the form who can testify that a breakage or spillage occurred.

      b. Must be done in compliance with all state and federal laws, and the method of destruction shall be sufficient to render all such controlled substances non-retrievable. Because this is difficult to do, most community pharmacies do not use this method of destruction.

      c. "Non-retrievable" is defined as "to permanently alter any controlled substance's physical and/or chemical condition or state through irreversible means in order to render the controlled substance unavailable and unusable for all practical purposes."

      Note: This can be difficult to execute. In addition to the difficulty of complying with other laws such as EPA laws, DEA has stated that methods such as mixing controlled substances with items such as kitty litter or coffee grounds and depositing them in the garbage do not meet the non-retrievable standard.

      d. PBOP Rule 49 Pa. Code § 27.14(b)(3-4) requires any pharmacy desiring to or required to dispose of a controlled substance to contact the nearest DEA office for authority and instructions. The pharmacist manager is

U. S. DEPARTMENT OF JUSTICE – DRUG ENFORCEMENT ADMINISTRATION
REGISTRANT RECORD OF CONTROLLED SUBSTANCES DESTROYED
FORM DEA-41

A. REGISTRANT INFORMATION

Registered Name:	DEA Registration Number:
Registered Address:	
City: State:	Zip Code:
Telephone Number:	Contact Name:

B. ITEM DESTROYED
1. Inventory

	National Drug Code or DEA Controlled Substances Code Number	Batch Number	Name of Substance	Strength	Form	Pkg. Qty.	Number of Full Pkgs.	Partial Pkg. Count	Total Destroyed
Examples	16590-598-60	N/A	Kadian	60mg	Capsules	60	2	0	120 Capsules
	0555-0767-02	N/A	Adderall	5mg	Tablet	100	0	83	83 Tablets
	9050	B02120312	Codeine	N/A	Bulk	1.25 kg	N/A	N/A	1.25 kg
1.									
2.									
3.									
4.									
5.									
6.									
7.									

2. Collected Substances

	Returned Mail-Back Package	Sealed Inner Liner	Unique Identification Number	Size of Sealed Inner Liner	Quantity of Packages(s)/Liner(s) Destroyed
Examples	X		MBP1106, MBP1108 - MBP1110, MBP112	N/A	5
		X	CRL1007 - CRL1027	15 gallon	21
		X	CRL1201	5 gallon	1
1.					
2.					
3.					
4.					
5.					
6.					
7.					

Form DEA-41   *See instructions on reverse (page 2) of form.*

DEA-41 Pg. 2

C. METHOD OF DESTRUCTION

Date of Destruction:	Method of Destruction:		
Location or Business Name:			
Address:			
City:	State:	Zip Code:	

D. WITNESSES

I declare under penalty of perjury, pursuant to 18 U.S.C. 1001, that I personally witnessed the destruction of the above-described controlled substances to a non-retrievable state and that all of the above is true and correct.

Printed name of first authorized employee witness:	Signature of first witness:	Date:
Printed name of second authorized employee witness:	Signature of second witness:	Date:

E. INSTRUCTIONS

1. Section A. REGISTRANT INFORMATION: The registrant destroying the controlled substance(s) shall provide their DEA registration number and the name and address indicated on their valid DEA registration, in addition to a current telephone number and a contact name, if different from the name on the valid DEA registration.

2. Section B. (1) Inventory: This part shall be used by registrants destroying lawfully possessed controlled substances, other than those described in Section B(2). In each row, indicate the National Drug Code (NDC) for the controlled substance destroyed, or if the substance has no NDC, indicate the DEA Controlled Substances Code Number for the substance; if the substance destroyed is in bulk form, indicate the batch number, if available. In each row, indicate the name, strength, and form of the controlled substance destroyed, and the number of capsules, tablets, etc., that are in a full package (pkg. qty.). If destroying the full quantity of the controlled substance, indicate the number of packages destroyed (number of full pkgs.). If destroying a partial package, indicate the partial count of the capsules, tablets, etc. destroyed (partial pkg. count). If destroying a controlled substance in bulk form, indicate that the substance is in bulk form (form) and the weight of the substance destroyed (pkg. qty.). In each row, indicate the total number of each controlled substance destroyed (total destroyed).

3. Section B. (2) Collected Substances: This part shall be used by registrants destroying controlled substances obtained through an authorized collection activity in accordance with 21 U.S.C. 822(g). In each row, indicate whether registrant is destroying a mail-back package or an inner liner. If destroying a mail-back package, enter each unique identification number separated by a comma and/or as a list in a sequential range and total quantity of packages being destroyed. If destroying an inner liner, enter each unique identification number separated by a comma and/or as a list in a sequential range based on the size of the liners destroyed and the total quantity of inner liners being destroyed. In the case of mail-back packages or inner liners received from a law enforcement agency which do not have a unique identification number or clearly marked size, include the name of the law enforcement agency and, if known, the size of the inner liner or package. DO NOT OPEN ANY MAIL-BACK PACKAGE OR INNER LINER; AN INVENTORY OF THE CONTENTS OF THE PACKAGES OR LINERS IS PROHIBITED BY LAW AND IS NOT REQUIRED BY THIS FORM.

4. If additional space is needed for items destroyed in Section B, attach to this form additional page(s) containing the requested information for each controlled substance destroyed.

5. Section C. METHOD OF DESTRUCTION: Provide the date, location, and method of destruction. The method of destruction must render the controlled substance to a state of non-retrievable and meet all applicable destruction requirements.

6. Section D. WITNESSES: Two authorized employees must declare by signature, under penalty of perjury, that such employees personally witnessed the destruction of the controlled substances listed in Section B in the manner described in Section C.

7. You are not required to submit this form to DEA, unless requested to do so. This form must be kept as a record of destruction and be available by the registrant for at least two years in accordance with 21 U.S.C. 827.

Paperwork Reduction Act Statement: The information collected on this form is necessary for DEA registrants to record controlled substances destroyed in accordance with the Controlled Substances Act (CSA). The records that DEA registrants maintain in accordance with the CSA must be kept and be available, for at least two years, for inspection and copying by officers or employees of the United States authorized by the Attorney General. 21 U.S.C. 827. DEA estimates that it will take approximately 30 minutes to complete this form, including the time for reviewing instructions, searching existing data sources, gathering and maintaining the data needed, and completing and reviewing the collection of information. The completion of this form by DEA registrants that destroy controlled substances is mandatory in accordance with 21 U.S.C. 827. Please note that an agency may not conduct or sponsor, and a person is not required to respond to, a collection of information unless it displays a currently valid OMB control number. Comments regarding this information collection, including suggestions for reducing the burden estimate, should be directed to the Drug Enforcement Administration, DEA Federal Register Representative/ODL, 8701 Morrissette Drive, Springfield, Virginia 22152.

responsible for keeping proper records of all disposed controlled substances, which must include the name of the substance, the number of units or the volume of the substance, or the number of commercial containers and the date and manner of disposal.

2. Transfer to an Authorized (Registered) Reverse Distributor
   a. This is the preferred method of destruction of controlled substance inventory in a pharmacy and is simply a transfer from one DEA registrant (the pharmacy) to another (the reverse distributor).
   b. Because this is a transfer, DEA Form 41 is not required. The transfer must be documented with an invoice for Schedule III–V controlled substances and DEA Form 222 for Schedule II controlled substances.

STUDY TIP: Be sure you understand the difference between the use of DEA Form 41, which is used to destroy controlled substances on the premises of a pharmacy (even though this is not often done in community practice), and transferring controlled substances to a DEA-registered reverse distributor for destruction, which requires DEA Form 222 or an invoice.

F. Disposal of Dispensed Controlled Substances Collected from Ultimate Users and Other Non-Registrants
   1. Authorized Collectors and DEA Take-Back Events
      a. DEA rules allow pharmacies to modify their DEA registrations to serve as a collector of dispensed controlled substances from ultimate users, including patients, the personal representative of the patient in the event of the patient's death, and at long-term care facilities.
      b. A pharmacy or hospital is not required to serve as a collector.
      c. The following rules apply to Authorized Collectors:
         (1) Collectors may allow ultimate users (patients) to deposit controlled substances into collection receptacles at the registered location or at an authorized long-term care facility (LTCF).
         (2) The controlled substances may be commingled with non-controlled substances.
         (3) The deposited substances may not be counted, sorted, inventoried, or individually handled. This

means that the pharmacist should not be handling these controlled substances on the patient's behalf. Patients must be the ones who place the controlled substances into the collection receptacles.

(4) LTCF staff may dispose of a patient's controlled substances into an authorized collection receptacle. Disposal into a collection receptacle must occur within three business days after the discontinuation of use by the patient.

(5) Collection receptacles must be in the immediate proximity (where they can be seen) of where controlled substances are stored (i.e., the pharmacy).

(6) Collection receptacles must be securely fastened to a permanent structure, locked, and securely constructed with a permanent outer container and a removable inner container.

(7) The inner liner must be waterproof, tamper-evident, removable, and able to be sealed immediately upon removal with no emptying or touching of the contents or ability to view the contents. The inner liner also must have a permanent unique identification number that allows tracking.

(8) The inner liner must be removed by or under the supervision of at least two employees of the Authorized Collector.

(9) Sealed inner liners may not be opened, x-rayed, analyzed, or otherwise penetrated.

(10) Collectors can either destroy the collected drugs on-site, transfer the collected drugs for final disposal to a DEA-registered reverse distributor, or contact the DEA Special Agent in Charge for assistance. If destroyed on-site, DEA Form 41 would be utilized. Section 2 of DEA Form 41 is for "collected substances." Instead of indicating the specific controlled substances being destroyed, it requires the unique identification number of the inner liner from the collection receptacle or the mail-back package.

d. A pharmacy that serves as a collector may also operate a mail-back program for collection of dispensed controlled substances. Packages used in a mail-back program must:

    (1) Be nondescript and not have any markings or other information that might indicate that the package contains controlled substances;

    (2) Be waterproof, tamper-evident, tear-resistant, and sealable;

    (3) Be pre-addressed with and delivered to the collector's registered address;

    (4) Include prepaid shipping costs;

    (5) Have a unique identification number to enable tracking; and

    (6) Include instructions for the user.

STUDY TIP: A collector that conducts a mail-back program may only accept packages that the collector made available. If the collector receives a package that it did not make available, the collector must notify DEA within three business days of receipt.

---

    e. DEA also conducts Drug Take Back Days to collect controlled substances (and other drugs) from ultimate users.

  2. Disposal of Controlled Substances of a Hospice Patient by Employees of the Hospice

    a. The SUPPORT Act, a comprehensive opioid bill passed by Congress in late 2018, authorizes an employee of a qualified hospice program to handle controlled substances that were lawfully dispensed to a person receiving hospice care, for the purpose of destruction.

    b. DEA has yet to adopt regulations to implement this law.

G. Inventories

  1. An initial inventory is required on the first day the pharmacy is open for business.

  2. Both federal and Pennsylvania law require a controlled substance inventory biennially (every 2 years) and that inventory must be maintained in the pharmacy.

  3. Newly scheduled drugs or drugs moved from one schedule to another must be inventoried on the day scheduled or moved to a new schedule.

4. Inventory Counts
    a. An exact count is required for all Schedule IIs.
    b. An estimated count is allowed for Schedule III–V products unless the container holds more than 1,000 tablets or capsules.

STUDY TIP: Although many pharmacies maintain a perpetual inventory of Schedule II controlled substances or even for all controlled substances, a perpetual inventory is not legally required.

H. Records
    1. Records of controlled substances must be maintained for 2 years under both the federal and Pennsylvania controlled substances acts.
    2. DEA requires that records and inventories of Schedule II controlled substances be kept separately from all other records. Records and inventories of Schedule III–V controlled substances must be maintained separately or be "readily retrievable" from other records. "Readily retrievable" means the record is kept or maintained in such a manner that it can be separated out from all other records in a reasonable time or that it is identified by an asterisk, a redline, or some other identifiable manner such that it is easily distinguishable from all other records.
    3. Records of Receipt of Controlled Substances
        a. C-II—Copy 3 of DEA Form 222 or copy of original single page DEA Form 222 (with the number of containers and date received filled in).
        b. C-III–C-V—Supplier's invoice.
    4. Records of Disbursement of Controlled Substances
        a. Most pharmacies maintain records of dispensing in an electronic system (i.e., computer system). DEA has specific requirements for electronic records of prescriptions as follows:
            (1) The electronic system must provide online retrieval of original prescription information and current refill history for those prescriptions which are currently authorized for refill.
            (2) The pharmacist must verify and document that the refill data entered into the system is correct.

(3) The system must be able to produce a hard-copy print-out of each day's controlled substance prescription refills, and each pharmacist who refilled those prescriptions must verify his/her accuracy by signing and dating the printout as he/she would sign a check or legal document. This daily printout must be printed within 72 hours of the date refills were dispensed. *Note: Most pharmacies do not print out this daily hard copy and instead use the alternative procedure in (4) below.*

(4) Instead of the daily printout, a pharmacy can maintain a bound logbook or a separate file in which each pharmacist involved in the day's dispensing signs a statement verifying that the refill information entered into the computer that day has been reviewed by him/her and is correct as shown.

(5) A pharmacy's electronic system must have the capability of printing out any refill data, which the pharmacy must maintain under the CSA. For example, this would include a refill-by-refill audit trail for any specified strength and dosage form of any controlled substance, by either brand or generic name or both, dispensed by the pharmacy. Such a printout must include:

  (i) Prescribing practitioner's name;

  (ii) Patient's name and address;

  (iii) Quantity and date dispensed on each refill;

  (iv) Name or identification code of the dispensing pharmacist; and

  (v) Original prescription number.

b. Pennsylvania has a similar rule for computerized recordkeeping systems used by a pharmacy for all dispensed prescriptions. *See PBOP Rule 49 Pa. Code § 27.202*

STUDY TIP: These are antiquated rules, but you need to know them. These rules were put in place when pharmacies were transitioning from manual recordkeeping to electronic recordkeeping. In a manual recordkeeping system, DEA rules still require the pharmacist to document all refills of controlled substances on the back of the hard copy of the prescription by indicating both the date refilled and the pharmacist's initials.

---

c. Prescription files—Although most pharmacies maintain electronic dispensing records, there are still specific storage requirements for the hard copies of all written or verbal controlled substance prescriptions that were reduced to writing. Storage options:

(1) 3-file storage system:
File #1 = Schedule II only.
File #2 = Schedule III–V.
File #3 = Other (non-controlled) drugs.

(2) 2-file storage system:
File #1 = Schedule II only.
File #2 = Schedule III–V and other (non-controlled) drugs. With this system, controlled substance prescriptions have to be stamped with red ink in the lower right corner of the prescription with a "C" (not less than 1 inch in height) so as to be readily retrievable from non-controlled substances.

Note: If a pharmacy maintains records in a data processing system for prescriptions (i.e., a computer) that permits identification by prescription number and retrieval of original documents by prescriber's name, patient's name, drug dispensed, and date filled, then the requirement to mark the hard-copy prescription with a red "C" is waived. See PCSDDCR 28 Pa. Code § 25.56 and 40 Pa. Bulletin 7160, Dec. 11, 2010

STUDY TIP: The file storage system requirements only apply to written prescriptions and verbal prescriptions that are reduced to writing by a pharmacist. If a controlled substance prescription is transmitted electronically, DEA requires that those electronic prescriptions be maintained electronically.

Other records of disbursement (i.e., controlled substances that leave a pharmacy) include DEA Form 106 (Theft or Significant Loss), DEA Form 41 (Destruction), DEA Form 222 for any Schedule II distributions made under the 5% rule, and invoices for Schedule III–V distributions made under the 5% rule.

I. Central Recordkeeping

1. A pharmacy wishing to maintain shipping and financial records at a central location other than the registered location must notify the nearest DEA Diversion Field Office.

2. Unless the pharmacy is notified by DEA that permission to keep the central records is denied, the pharmacy may begin maintaining central records 14 days after notifying DEA.
3. Central records shall not include executed (i.e., completed) DEA order forms (the copy made by the pharmacy of single copy DEA Form 222), prescriptions, or inventories. These must be kept at the pharmacy.

STUDY TIP: Notice that unused DEA Form 222s may be kept at a central location, but once they have been executed (i.e., completed), the copy of the form that is made must be kept at the pharmacy. This is because that copy of the DEA order form is where the pharmacist documents receipt of the product, and that becomes the official record of the Schedule II controlled substances received. Be sure to know the records that cannot be kept at a central location.

VI. Dispensing Controlled Substance Prescriptions
A. Corresponding Responsibility
1. For a prescription for a controlled substance to be valid, it must be issued for a legitimate medical purpose by an individual practitioner acting in the usual scope of his or her professional practice.
2. The responsibility for the proper prescribing and dispensing of a controlled substance is upon the prescribing practitioner, but a corresponding responsibility rests with the pharmacist who fills the prescription. This means a pharmacist cannot knowingly fill a prescription that was not issued for a legitimate medical purpose. A pharmacist cannot simply rely on the fact that a physician has a valid DEA registration to determine if a controlled substance prescription is valid.
3. DEA considers a pharmacist who deliberately ignores a "high probability" that a prescription was not issued for a legitimate medical purpose and fills the prescription to have met the knowledge requirement. A pharmacist who does so may be prosecuted along with the issuing practitioner for knowingly and intentionally distributing controlled substances.
4. Through enforcement actions, DEA has identified a number of "red flags" that may require a pharmacist to do further

investigation as to the legitimacy of controlled substance prescriptions. Examples of potential red flags include:

    a. Multiple customers filling prescriptions written by the same prescriber for the same drugs in the same quantities;

    b. Customers with the same last name and street address presenting similar prescriptions on the same day or within a short time span;

    c. Two short-acting opiates prescribed together;

    d. Patients traveling long distances to fill opioid prescriptions;

    e. Drug cocktails;

    f. Payment by cash;

    g. Unusually large quantity of controlled substances;

    h. Pattern prescribing;

    i. Irregular dosing instructions;

    j. Lack of individualized therapy or dosing;

    k. Early fills/refills.

B. Prescriptive Authority

    1. Who can prescribe controlled substance prescriptions is determined by state law. Pennsylvania law authorizes the following practitioners to prescribe controlled substances if they have a valid DEA registration number:

        a. Medical Doctors licensed under the Medical Practice Act (63 P. S. §§ 422.1–422.45) (M.D.)

        b. Osteopathic physicians licensed under the Osteopathic Medical Practice Act (63 P. S. §§ 271.1–271.18) (D.O.)

        c. Dentists licensed under the Dental Law (63 P. S. §§ 120–130b) (D.D.S. or D.M.D.)

        d. Podiatrists licensed under the Podiatry Act (63 P. S. §§ 42.1–42.21a) (D.P.M.)

        e. Veterinarians licensed under the Veterinary Medicine Practice Act (63 P. S. §§ 485.1–485.33) (D.V.M.)

        f. Certified Optometrists licensed under the Optometric Practice and Licensure Act (63 P. S. §§ 244.1–244.12) (O.D.)

        Note: Optometrists that are certified to prescribe and administer pharmaceutical agents for therapeutic purposes have a limited formulary that includes a few controlled substance medications for analgesic use (codeine in combination with acetaminophen or aspirin, hydrocodone in combination with acetaminophen or ibuprofen [not to exceed a 72-hour supply], pentazocine, and tramadol). For general rules on prescriptions from certified optometrists, see Chapter 3, Section II. A.5.

STUDY TIP: Other healthcare practitioners such as chiropractors may be licensed by the Pennsylvania Department of State and considered mid-level practitioners, but they do not have prescriptive authority.

---

g. Physician Assistants licensed under the Medical Practice Act or the Osteopathic Medical Practice Act (PA)
Note: For general rules on prescriptions from Physician Assistants, see Chapter 3, Section II. A.2.
Controlled substance specific rules are as follows:
   (1) Authority to prescribe controlled substances must be delegated by supervising physician.
   (2) Schedule II controlled substances are limited to a 72-hour dose for initial therapy and a 30-day supply for ongoing therapy. The prescription must clearly state on its face that it is for initial or ongoing therapy.
h. Certified Registered Nurse Practitioners licensed under the Professional Nursing Law (63 P. S. §§ 211–225.5) (CRNP)
Note: For general rules on prescriptions from CRNPs, see Chapter 3, Section II. A.3.
Controlled substance specific rules are as follows:
   (1) Authority to prescribe controlled substances must be delegated by supervising physician.
   (2) Schedule II controlled substances are limited to a 30-day supply as identified in a collaborative agreement.
   (3) Schedule III or IV controlled substances can be prescribed up to a 90-day supply as identified in the collaborative agreement.
i. Nurse Midwives licensed under the Medical Practice Act (CNM)
   (1) Authority to prescribe controlled substances must be delegated by supervising physician. A nurse-midwife may prescribe Schedule II–V controlled substances for a woman's acute pain.

        (2) Schedule II controlled substances are limited to 72 hours and may not be extended without the approval of the collaborating physician.

        (3) Schedule III–V controlled substances may only be prescribed up to a 30-day supply and can only be refilled with the approval of the collaborating physician.

        (4) Psychotropic drugs may only be prescribed after consulting with the collaborating physician.

2. Out-of-State Prescribers

    a. Pennsylvania law does not expressly prohibit accepting prescriptions from out-of-state prescribers. The PPA defines a "prescription" as a written or oral order issued by a duly licensed medical practitioner in the course of their professional practice for a controlled substance, other drug, or device or medication that is dispensed for use by a consumer. "Medical practitioner" is defined as a physician, dentist, veterinarian, or other individual duly authorized and licensed by law to prescribe drugs.

    b. The Pennsylvania Department of Health has provided that a Pennsylvania dispenser may legally accept an out-of-state electronic prescription for a controlled substance, and that it is prudent on the part of the pharmacist to verify the authenticity of any controlled substance prescription presented to them.

3. Out-of-Country Practitioners

    a. Controlled substances prescriptions—A practitioner in another country cannot have a DEA registration; therefore, any prescription for a controlled substance issued in another country is not permitted.

    b. Non-controlled substance prescriptions—It is less clear for non-controlled substances, but it is generally considered not acceptable to accept and dispense prescriptions from foreign doctors. Without a definitive statement in the laws and rules that permit prescriptions from out of the country, it is likely that such prescriptions are not valid.

4. Designated Agents

    a. Can communicate a prescription for a C-III–C-V controlled substance but cannot authorize or prescribe.

    b. Can prepare a written prescription for the signature of the practitioner.

    c. Can transmit a signed written controlled substance prescription by fax to a pharmacy (where permitted by regulations).

    d. An authorized agent of the prescriber (employee or non-employee) may not verbally communicate emergency C-II prescriptions to a pharmacist. This task cannot be delegated.

    e. DEA requires that for non-employees of the prescriber to qualify as an agent of the prescriber, there must be a formal written appointment of the agent by the prescriber. This is important for facilities such as nursing homes, where the nurses may not be employees of the physician but may wish to call in a prescription to a pharmacy on behalf of a physician.

    f. The DEA also believes it is in the best interest of the prescriber and the agent that the designation of those persons authorized to act on behalf of the prescriber and the scope of any such authorization be reduced to writing. A signed copy should also be provided to the practitioner's designated agent, the agent's employer (if other than the practitioner), and any pharmacies that regularly receive communications from the agent pursuant to the agreement. To help prevent against fraud, the DEA recommends pharmacists know the prescriber's authorized agents and request a copy of any written agreement between the prescriber and their agent.

C. Mandatory Electronic Prescriptions for Controlled Substances

    1. Pennsylvania passed legislation (PA Act 96 of 2018) requiring prescribers to issue all controlled substance prescriptions electronically.

    2. This requirement became effective October 24, 2019, and the Pennsylvania Department of Health is in the process of promulgating regulations in accordance with the law. While the Department of Health works to promulgate regulations, it is accepting petitions for temporary exemptions from the requirements of Act 96.

    3. In addition to any temporary waivers, electronic prescriptions are also not required under the law when:

a. The prescription is issued by a veterinarian;
b. The prescription cannot be transmitted electronically due to a temporary technological or electrical failure (practitioner has 72 hours to correct the technological failure);
c. The prescription is issued by a practitioner and dispensed by a pharmacy outside of Pennsylvania;
d. A practitioner or healthcare facility does not have internet access or an electronic health record system, or the pharmacy is not set up to process electronic prescriptions;
e. The practitioner is treating a patient in an emergency department or a healthcare facility under circumstances when the practitioner reasonably determines that electronically prescribing a controlled substance would be impractical for the patient to obtain the controlled substance prescribed by electronic prescription or would cause an untimely delay resulting in an adverse impact on the patient's medical condition;
f. The prescription is for a patient enrolled in a hospice program or for a patient residing in a nursing home or residential healthcare facility;
g. The prescription is issued for an emergency situation pursuant to federal and/or state law; or
h. The controlled substance being prescribed is not required to be reported to the state PDMP.

STUDY TIP: Because of the many exceptions to the mandatory electronic prescription requirements, you may still see questions about written, verbal, and faxed prescriptions for controlled substances on the MPJE.

D. Written Controlled Substance Prescriptions
  1. Must be manually signed by the practitioner and dated on the date issued.
  2. Must contain:
    a. The full name and address of the patient;
    b. The drug name, strength, and dosage form;
    c. The quantity prescribed;
    d. Directions for use;
    e. Number of refills authorized, if any (not for Schedule II);
    f. The name, address, and DEA number of the practitioner;

    g. If written for a Schedule II prescription to be filled at a later date, the earliest date on which a pharmacy may fill a prescription; and

    h. The PBOP requires all written controlled substance prescriptions filled and filed to have a prescription number, the name or initials of the dispensing pharmacist, cautions communicated to the ultimate user, and the date filled. *See PBOP Rule 49 Pa. Code § 27.18(b)*

E. Verbal, Fax, and Electronic Prescriptions

    1. Verbal prescriptions are not valid for Schedule II controlled substances unless it is an emergency.

    2. Verbal prescriptions are valid for Schedule III–V controlled substances.

    3. Fax prescriptions are valid for Schedule III–V controlled substances but must have the prescriber's original signature. Electronic signatures are not valid on faxed controlled substance prescriptions. Faxes for Schedule II controlled substances are only allowed in limited circumstances. *See Section VII. B. below*

    4. Electronic prescriptions for controlled substances (including Schedule II) are valid if both the prescriber's computer and the pharmacy's computer meet all DEA security requirements.

VII. Schedule II Prescriptions

A. General

    1. Schedule II prescriptions must be either written or electronically submitted.

    2. Verbal prescriptions for Schedule II drugs are not permitted except in an emergency. *See C. below*

    3. Schedule II prescriptions cannot be refilled.

    4. There is no time limit under federal law as to when a Schedule II prescription must be filled after being issued by the practitioner. However, under PBOP rules, prescriptions for

Schedule II controlled substances may not be filled more than 6 months from the date of the prescription. *See PBOP Rule 49 Pa. Code § 27.18(j)*

STUDY TIP: Although Schedule II prescriptions can be filled up to 6 months from the date of issuance, the pharmacist must use professional judgment and exercise their corresponding responsibility before dispensing a controlled substance prescription to ensure it is valid.

---

5. Quantity Limits on Schedule II Prescriptions
   a. There is not a specific quantity limit for all Schedule II controlled substances on a single prescription under federal or Pennsylvania law.
   b. All prescribers in Pennsylvania are subject to quantity limits when prescribing Schedule II opioid products for acute pain. *See E. below*
   c. Mid-level prescribers are limited in the quantity of Schedule II controlled substances they can prescribe. *See Section VI. B. above*
   d. There is a 90-day supply limit when a practitioner issues multiple Schedule II prescriptions the same day. *See 6. below*
   e. Although there is technically no quantity limit on a single controlled substance prescription, pharmacists should exercise their corresponding responsibility on every prescription to ensure it is legitimate. Insurance plans or pharmacy policies may limit the amount that may be filled on a single prescription, but these are not legal requirements.
6. Changing Information or Information Omitted
   a. DEA provided guidance to the profession and state boards of pharmacies in 2011 regarding information a pharmacist may add or change on a written Schedule II prescription. DEA stated that whether a pharmacist may make changes to a Schedule II prescription—such as adding the practitioner's DEA number, or correcting the patient's name or address—varies case by case based on the facts present. Thus, "DEA expects that when information is missing from or needs to be changed on a Schedule II controlled substance prescription, pharmacists use their professional judgment and knowledge of

state and federal laws and policies to decide whether it is appropriate to make changes to that prescription." DEA also stated that pharmacists should rely on state rules and guidance in making any such changes. The DEA removed this guidance from their website a few years ago; however, pharmacists should still rely on state rules and guidance in making any changes or additions.

b. Pennsylvania does provide guidance on this matter as it pertains to incorrect or missing information for electronically prescribed controlled substances (which are now required for all controlled substance prescriptions in Pennsylvania, with exceptions). The Pennsylvania guidance provides:

(1) Information added/changed on an electronic prescription must be annotated and maintained electronically. Dispensers should consult their software vendor or corporate headquarters for guidance to ensure annotation meets all federal requirements. The process of annotating a prescription may vary based on the software used.

(2) When a prescription prepared by a practitioner is incomplete, the practitioner may orally furnish the missing information to the pharmacist and authorize him or her to enter the missing information on the prescription. The pharmacist shall write the date he or she received the oral authorization on the prescription and shall affix his or her signature.

(3) This procedure just provided shall not apply to unsigned or undated prescriptions or where the name and/or quantity of the controlled substance is not specified or where the name of the ultimate user is missing.

(4) The pharmacist is not required to obtain authorization from the practitioner to enter the patient's address, sex, or age if the pharmacist obtains this information through a good-faith effort, such as from the patient or caregiver.

7. Multiple Prescriptions for Schedule II Drugs (DEA Rule 21 CFR 1306.12(b)(1))

a. DEA permits an individual practitioner to issue multiple Schedule II prescriptions on the same day, authorizing the patient to receive a total of no more than a 90-day supply of a Schedule II controlled substance. Instructions indicating the earliest fill date on which the prescriptions can be filled must be on each prescription.

    b. This 90-day limit only applies when the prescriber is issuing multiple prescriptions for a Schedule II controlled substance on the same day, with instructions that some of the prescriptions are not to be filled until a later date. *Note: Logically, if there is no quantity limit for a single Schedule II prescription, then there is no reason for this rule. Technically, that is correct, but in this case DEA realized that because many insurance plans don't cover more than a 30-day supply of controlled substances, patients would need to go to the prescriber every month to get a new written prescription for any Schedule II controlled substance since they could not be called in. This was before electronic prescriptions were more prevalent. Rather than having prescribers postdate a prescription, which DEA has never allowed and still does not allow, this rule was adopted. When it adopted this rule, DEA limited the total quantity to 90 days, but it has still not placed a days' supply limit on a single controlled substance prescription.*

STUDY TIP: The rules for issuing multiple Schedule II prescriptions seem to cause much confusion with pharmacy students and pharmacists. Be sure you understand this concept. These are not considered refills.

B. Facsimile Prescriptions for Schedule II Controlled Substances
    1. Facsimiles are generally not valid for Schedule II prescriptions.
    2. However, DEA and Pennsylvania (*see PBOP Rule 49 Pa. Code § 27.20(a)*) recognize three exceptions where a facsimile can serve as the original written prescription:
        a. A practitioner prescribing a Schedule II narcotic for a patient undergoing home infusion/IV pain therapy;
        b. A practitioner prescribing a Schedule II controlled substance for patients in Long Term Care Facilities (LTCFs); and
        c. A practitioner prescribing a Schedule II narcotic for a patient in hospice care.

C. Emergency Dispensing of a Schedule II Controlled Substance Pursuant to a Verbal Prescription

    1. In an emergency situation, a practitioner may provide a verbal Schedule II prescription to a pharmacy.

STUDY TIP: Communication must be from the prescriber and not a designated agent.

---

    2. "Emergency" means that the immediate administration of the drug is necessary for the proper treatment of the ultimate user, that no alternative treatment is available, and that it is not possible for the prescribing practitioner to provide a written prescription.

    3. The quantity prescribed and dispensed is limited to the amount needed to treat the patient during the emergency period.

    4. The prescription order must be immediately reduced to writing by the pharmacist and contain all information except the practitioner's signature.

    5. If the prescriber is not known to the pharmacist, the pharmacist must make a reasonable effort to determine that the phone authorization came from a valid practitioner.

    6. Within 3 days after authorizing an emergency telephone prescription, the prescribing practitioner must furnish the pharmacist with a signed or a valid electronic prescription for the controlled substance prescribed (if mailed, it must be postmarked within 3 days). The prescription should be marked "Authorization for Emergency Dispensing."
Note: Federal law is 7 days, while Pennsylvania law is 3 days (28 Pa. Code § 25.45).

    7. If the prescriber fails to deliver a written or electronic prescription, the pharmacist must notify the nearest DEA office.

STUDY TIP: Remember, under Pennsylvania law the prescribing practitioner must provide the pharmacist with the signed written or electronic Schedule II prescription within 3 days. This is different from federal law.

D. Partial Dispensing of a Schedule II Controlled Substance Prescription

    1. 72-Hour Rule

        a. If a pharmacist is unable to fill the entire quantity on a Schedule II controlled substance prescription, a partial quantity may be provided so long as the remaining quantity is ready for dispensing prior to the 72-hour time limit; however, the patient is not required to pick up the balance of the prescription within that 72-hour time limit.

    b. If the remaining quantity cannot be provided, the pharmacist must notify the prescriber.

2. 30-Day Rule

    a. Under the Comprehensive Addiction and Recovery Act (CARA) of 2016, federal law was modified to allow partial fills of Schedule II controlled substances for up to 30 days if requested by the patient of the prescriber.

    b. The total quantity dispensed may not exceed the original quantity prescribed.

    c. This applies to written and electronic prescriptions, but not to emergency verbal Schedule II controlled substance prescriptions. For emergency verbal Schedule II prescriptions, the 72-hour rule above must be followed for a partial fill.

3. 60-Day Rule

    a. For terminally ill and LTCF patients, both federal law and Pennsylvania law allow partial fills of Schedule II prescriptions as many times as needed as long as the partial fillings are recorded on the prescription or maintained in the pharmacy's computer system.

    b. All partial fills for terminally ill and LTCF patients must be completed within 60 days.

STUDY TIP: Be sure you understand the difference between a partial fill and a refill. Partial fills are not considered full refills. Remember, there are no refills on a Schedule II controlled substance prescription.

E. Pennsylvania Restrictions on the Treatment of Acute Pain

1. General Information

    a. In response to the opioid epidemic, the Pennsylvania Legislature passed 2 laws that placed opioid prescribing limits on certain patient populations and in certain practice settings.

    b. Additional laws have been proposed in Pennsylvania that would further expand the opioid prescribing limitations to most adults in most practice settings. However, even without these laws, there are still various state issued prescribing and dispensing practice guidelines, public and private insurance limits, and pharmacy policies in place that limit the quantities of opioids being dispensed for acute pain for most if not all patients. The Pennsylvania Department of Health opioid prescribing and dispensing guidelines for acute and chronic pain can be found at the Pennsylvania Department of Health website, *https://www.health.pa.gov/topics/disease/Opioids/Pages/Prescribing-Guidelines.aspx*.

2. Pennsylvania Act 122 of 2016 (Safe Emergency Prescribing Act) and Act 125 of 2016 (Prescribing Opioids to Minors)

   a. Act 122 requires opioid prescription practices for prescribers in emergency department, urgent care, and hospital observation settings. Prescribers can prescribe up to a 7-day supply of an opioid medication to a patient seeking treatment in an emergency department or urgent care facility or in observation status in a hospital. Exceptions include if additional opioid drugs are needed for palliative care, cancer treatment, or to treat a patient's acute condition. However, the condition triggering the extension and an indication that a non-opioid treatment is not appropriate must be documented in the patient's medical record. Prescribers in emergency departments or urgent care centers or those caring for patients under observation status in hospitals may not refill prescriptions for opioid and opioid-like products.

   b. Act 125 provides that a prescriber cannot prescribe an opioid medication to a minor unless it is needed for a clearly documented medical emergency or if the prescriber determines that not using opioids would be detrimental to the minor's health and safety. Prior to prescribing up to a 7-day limit, the prescriber must obtain the written consent of his/her parent or guardian and discuss various risk factors of taking opioids with the minor and parent. If consent is given by a minor's authorized adult, the prescription is limited to a single 72-hour supply. There are exceptions to the 7-day prescribing limit, including treatment associated with cancer, palliative care, or the management of chronic pain not associated with cancer.

VIII. Schedule III–V Prescriptions

With so many exceptions to the electronic prescribing mandate for controlled substances, pharmacists need to know the requirements for written, faxed, and verbal Schedule III–V prescriptions.

A. General Rules
1. May be filled from written, verbal, and facsimile prescriptions.
2. May be filled from electronic prescriptions as long as all DEA security requirements are met.
3. May be refilled as indicated on the original prescription up to 5 times in the 6-month period from the date of the prescription.

B. Transfers
1. Refills of Schedule III–V controlled substances may be transferred to another pharmacy on a onetime basis.
2. If pharmacies share an electronic, real-time, online database of prescriptions, they may transfer up to the maximum number of refills permitted by law and the prescriber's authorization.
3. Only refills may be transferred. DEA rules do not permit a pharmacy to transfer to another pharmacy an original controlled substance prescription that has been received at a pharmacy but not yet filled. An exception to this is permitted by DEA policy that allows an original electronic prescription for a controlled substance (EPCS), including a Schedule II prescription, to be transferred to another

pharmacy if both pharmacies have the capability to forward and receive the EPCS using an electronic sharing program. *Note: Although the procedure above is allowed by DEA policy, some pharmacies may choose not to do this, and some pharmacy computer systems do not have this capability.*

C. Sale of Schedule V Exempt Products

 1. The federal government allows certain Schedule V products to be purchased from a pharmacy without a prescription. The PCSDDCA rule mirrors the federal law and allows Schedule V products which are not prescription drugs as determined by the FDCA to be dispensed without a prescription, provided conditions are met. Conditions include quantity limits, age restrictions, and documentation requirements. *See 28 Pa. Code § 25.57*

 2. The PBOP has a regulation that requires a prescription before a pharmacist in the outpatient setting can dispense a Schedule V cough preparation containing codeine, dilaudid, or other narcotic. *See PBOP Rule 49 Pa. Code § 27.18(f).* Since the PBOP rule is stricter for Schedule V cough preparations, Pennsylvania pharmacists need to follow the stricter rule.

STUDY TIP: It is important to remember that Pennsylvania pharmacists in the outpatient setting must obtain a prescription to dispense Schedule V cough preparations.

D. Additional Pennsylvania Requirements for Schedule III–V Controlled Substances

 1. Pennsylvania provides additional details regarding the prescribing and dispensing of anabolic steroids, which are all classified as Schedule III. Specifically, Pennsylvania law states that a practitioner shall not prescribe, administer, or dispense any anabolic steroid for the purpose of 1. enhancing a person's performance in an exercise, sport, or game, or 2. hormonal manipulation intended to increase muscle mass, strength, or weight except when medically necessary.

 2. As with prescriptions for Schedule II controlled substances, some mid-level prescribers in Pennsylvania have limitations in prescribing Schedule III–V controlled substances. *See Section VI.*

IX. Methadone, Opiate Dependence, Naloxone, and Methamphetamine Controls

A. Prescribing and Dispensing of Certain Narcotic Drugs

1. Methadone is used both for the treatment of severe pain and in the detoxification and maintenance of narcotic addicts in registered narcotic treatment programs (also often called opioid treatment programs).

2. While any pharmacy can stock methadone, it can only legally be dispensed as an analgesic (for pain treatment).

3. DEA has requested manufacturers and wholesalers to voluntarily restrict sales of methadone 40 mg to hospitals and narcotic treatment clinics only; no sales to retail pharmacies are allowed.

4. Methadone (or any other drug) cannot be dispensed for the maintenance or detoxification of addicts unless it is provided through a registered narcotic treatment center.

5. Narcotic treatment facilities may administer and dispense (but not prescribe) narcotic drugs to a narcotic-dependent person for detoxification or maintenance treatment.

   a. Short-term detoxification means dispensing of a narcotic drug in decreasing doses for a period not to exceed 30 days.

   b. Long-term detoxification means dispensing of a narcotic drug to a narcotic-dependent person in decreasing doses in excess of 30 days but not in excess of 180 days.

STUDY TIP: Make sure you understand that a narcotic treatment program is a specific type of DEA registration that permits the administration and dispensing of methadone, but those practitioners may not write prescriptions such as methadone for treating addiction that can be filled at a pharmacy. Pharmacies may only dispense prescriptions for methadone for pain. It is acceptable to dispense a prescription for methadone as part of a formal pain management program in which a patient is switched to methadone to control or gradually reduce dosage of other narcotics, but methadone cannot be dispensed from a pharmacy solely as a treatment for opioid dependency.

---

6. A physician who is not part of a narcotic treatment program may administer (not prescribe) narcotic drugs (e.g., methadone) to an addicted individual for not more than a 3-day period until the individual can be enrolled in a narcotic treatment program.

7. A hospital that is not part of a narcotic treatment program may administer narcotics to a drug-dependent person for either detoxification or maintenance therapy if the patient is being treated in the hospital for a condition other than addiction.

B. Medication Assisted Treatment (MAT) for Opiate Dependence

1. The Drug Addiction Treatment Act of 2000 (DATA 2000) allows office-based, specially trained practitioners to prescribe certain narcotic Schedule III–V drugs to treat opiate dependence through a risk management program outside of a narcotic treatment facility.

2. A practitioner authorized to prescribe under the Act, called a Qualifying Practitioner (or DATA-waived practitioner), can apply for a DATA 2000 waiver if they meet specific criteria. The waiver is provided by the Substance Abuse and Mental Health Services Administration (SAMHSA), and the practitioner is provided a Unique Identification Number (UIN) or "X" number that must be included with the prescriber's DEA number. Pharmacists can verify a practitioner's DATA waiver at the SAMHSA website's Buprenorphine Pharmacy Lookup.
Note: The term "Qualifying Other Practitioner" is used for a nurse practitioner, a physician assistant, a clinical nurse specialist, certified registered nurse anesthetists, or certified nurse midwives that are also authorized to participate in MAT.

3. The only drugs that may be dispensed under this program are Subutex® (buprenorphine) and Suboxone® (buprenorphine/naloxone combination). These drugs, both Schedule III controlled substances, are available in sublingual form and may be dispensed by a pharmacy upon a prescription from a qualified practitioner.

4. A Qualifying Practitioner may be allowed to treat up to 30, 100, or 275 patients, depending on his or her authorization. An authorized nurse practitioner or physician assistant may initially treat up to 30 patients. After one year, the nurse practitioner or physician assistant may apply for authorization to treat up to 100 patients.

5. A pharmacy can deliver a controlled substance to a Qualifying (or Qualifying Other) Practitioner to administer the medication by injection or implantation to a patient for purposes of maintenance or detoxification. The controlled

substance must be administered to the patient within 14 days of delivery.

6. In order to encourage more practitioners to seek a DATA waiver, under practice guidelines issued by HHS on April 28, 2021, practitioners who limit their treatment to no more than 30 patients may apply for a waiver without having to meet certain certification requirements related to training, counseling, and other ancillary services (i.e., psychosocial services) that are normally required.

STUDY TIP: A Qualifying Practitioner can treat opioid addiction and prescribe MAT drugs (buprenorphine and buprenorphine/naloxone) from his or her office. They do not need to work at or be registered as a narcotic treatment program. Likewise, a practitioner that is part of a narcotic treatment program cannot automatically prescribe MAT drugs to be filled at a pharmacy. They would also need to be a Qualifying Practitioner.

STUDY TIP: The prescribing or dispensing of certain buprenorphine products for pain may be considered "off-label" use. In these circumstances, the "X" number is not required by the prescriber.

C. Dispensing of Naloxone in Pennsylvania
   Note: Although naloxone is not a controlled substance, it is included in this chapter since it concerns treatment of opioid addiction.
   1. The PCSDDCA was amended in 2014 (PA Act 139) to allow Pennsylvania-licensed pharmacists to dispense an emergency opioid antagonist such as naloxone based on a non-patient-specific standing order for an auto-injection delivery system or intranasal application delivery system.
   2. The State Physician General issued a statewide naloxone standing order for eligible individuals to use as a prescription to obtain naloxone from pharmacies in Pennsylvania.
   3. Pharmacies can use the standing order available through the Department of Public Health website to dispense naloxone to patients, caregivers, or others.
   4. A pharmacist, acting in good faith and exercising reasonable care, is not subject to discipline or other adverse action under any professional licensure statute or rule and is immune from any civil or criminal liability as a result of dispensing an emergency opioid antagonist.

D. The Combat Methamphetamine Epidemic Act of 2005

    1. This law was passed by Congress to further control the sale of OTC products containing precursor chemicals used in the illicit manufacturing of methamphetamine.

    2. The law classifies all products (including multiple-ingredient products) containing ephedrine, pseudoephedrine, and phenylpropanolamine as "listed chemical products."

    Note: Since this law was passed, ephedrine and phenylpropanolamine products have all been removed from the market by FDA, so the law really only impacts pseudoephedrine products.

    3. Products containing a "listed chemical" are subject to the following requirements:

        a. Display Restrictions—Although the products may be sold by any retailer, covered products must be placed behind a counter (not necessarily a pharmacy counter) or, if located on the selling floor, in a locked cabinet.

        b. Retail Sales Limits—Sales of covered products to an individual are limited to 3.6 g of the base product per day and 9 g of the base product per 30 days. Many states have sales limits per transaction.

        c. For pseudoephedrine HCL, the daily limit of 3.6 g of base product equals:

            (1) 146 of the 30 mg tablets.

            (2) 73 of the 60 mg tablets.

            (3) 36 of the 120 mg tablets.

        d. Product Packaging—Covered products (other than liquids including gel caps) must either be in blister or unit-dose packaging.

    4. Recordkeeping Requirements.

        a. Retailer must maintain an electronic or written logbook that identifies the products by name, quantity sold, names and addresses of purchasers, and dates and times of sales.

        b. There is an exception for the logbook requirement for individual sales of a single "convenience" package of less than 60 mg of pseudoephedrine.

        c. Purchaser must present a photo identification issued by a state or federal government, must sign logbook, and must enter his or her name, address, and date and time of sale.

        d. Retailer must verify that the name entered in the logbook corresponds to the customer identification.

5. Pennsylvania Requirements.
   a. Pennsylvania law (Act 53 of 2013) requires all pharmacies and retailers that sell OTC cold and allergy medications containing pseudoephedrine to participate in a state-wide, real-time electronic pseudoephedrine monitoring program for the purpose of tracking and blocking illegal pseudoephedrine purchases.
   b. Pennsylvania uses the National Precursor Log Exchange (NPLEx) system, which provides alerts when individuals attempt to purchase more than the legal limits of pseudoephedrine. Retailers/pharmacies must electronically submit the required information into NPLEx prior to completing a pseudoephedrine sale.
6. Employee Training.
   a. Employers certify that employees who deal directly with customers have undergone training to ensure they understand the requirements of the law.
   b. DEA requirements for self-certification and training can be found at *www.deadiversion.usdoj.gov/meth/index.html*.
7. Mail Service Limitations.
   a. Mail service companies must confirm the identity of purchasers.
   b. Sales are limited to 7.5 g per 30-day period.
8. Mobile Retail Vendors ("flea markets"):
   a. Product must be placed in a locked cabinet.
   b. Sales are limited to no more than 7.5 g of base product per customer per 30 days.
E. Dextromethorphan (DXM) Laws
   Note: DXM is not a scheduled controlled substance drug at the federal or Pennsylvania level; however, some states have started to regulate it due to its abuse potential. The MPJE also has a competency statement that addresses it.
   1. DXM is a legally marketed cough suppressant that is neither a controlled substance nor a regulated chemical under the FCSA. DXM is available as an OTC product or in combination with other medications as an OTC or prescription product.
   2. DXM is abused in high doses to experience euphoria and visual and auditory hallucinations.
   3. Several states have implemented and/or passed legislation prohibiting the sale or purchase of DXM products to persons under the age of 18.

4. Pennsylvania has passed a DXM law (Act 116 of 2018). Details of Act 116 include:
   a. A person commits a summary offense if he/she knowingly sells or purchases with the intent to sell a drug product containing DXM to a person under the age of 18.
   b. A person commits a summary offense if he/she falsely represents themself to be 18 years of age or older in order to obtain a product with any quantity of DXM.
   c. A person making a retail sale of a drug product containing any quantity of DXM must obtain proof of age from the purchaser prior to completing the sale, unless the individual's outward appearance is such that one would reasonably presume the purchaser to be at least 25 years of age.
   d. The requirements of the law do not apply to a medication containing DXM that is sold pursuant to a valid prescription.

X. The Pennsylvania Prescription Drug Monitoring Program (PDMP)
A. General Information
   1. The Pennsylvania PDMP, also known as the Achieving Better Care by Monitoring All Prescriptions (ABC-MAP) program, became effective after PA Act 124 2016 was passed. The program collects information on all filled controlled substance prescriptions and is run by the Pennsylvania Department of Health.
   2. The purpose of the PDMP is to have it be used as a tool to increase the quality of patient care by giving prescribers and dispensers access to a patient's controlled substance prescription medication history, which can alert medical professionals to potential dangers for purposes of making treatment determinations. Another purpose of the PDMP is to aid regulatory and law enforcement agencies in the detection and prevention of fraud, drug abuse, and criminal diversion of controlled substances.
   3. Dispensers, prescribers, and their delegates have "real-time" access to the data stored by the PDMP at any given time.
   4. The Pennsylvania PDMP is part of NABP's PMP Inter-Connect, allowing pharmacists to perform queries of a patient's controlled substance use in most other states.

B. Mandatory Registration and Use

1. All individuals lawfully authorized to dispense in Pennsylvania, including mail order and internet pharmacies, must register with the PDMP through the Pennsylvania Department of Health.

2. Dispensers may query the PDMP for a current patient to whom the dispenser is dispensing or considering dispensing any controlled substance.

3. Dispensers must query the PDMP before dispensing an opioid drug product or a benzodiazepine prescribed to a patient if any of the following apply:

    a. The patient is a new patient of the dispenser (patients that go to a different physical location of the same pharmacy that has access to patient records are excluded).

    b. The patient pays cash when they have insurance ("cash" refers to any non-insurance payment, excluding copays).

    c. The patient is getting opioid drug products or benzodiazepines from more than one prescriber.

    d. The patient requests an early refill (defined as prior to the date when they are eligible for insurance coverage for the prescription or when more than 15% of an earlier dispensed medication would remain when taken in compliance with the directions and quantity prescribed).

    e. The dispenser has reason to believe the patient is getting opioids or benzodiazepines from more than one prescriber.

STUDY TIP: A pharmacy cannot provide information from the PDMP to a law enforcement officer. A law enforcement agency would have to request information directly from the Pennsylvania Office of the Attorney General. The Office of the Attorney General shall query the system on behalf of all law enforcement agencies for Schedule II controlled substances and all other schedules upon receipt of a court order obtained by the requesting law enforcement agency.

C. Reporting Requirements

1. Dispensers, including pharmacies and dispensing prescribers, must submit all controlled substance (Schedules II–V) dispensing information to the PDMP no later than the close of the subsequent business day after dispensing a controlled substance.

2. Reporting to the PDMP has exemptions. The term "dispenser" does not include veterinarians, hospice providers, prescribers at a healthcare facility that dispense no more than a 5-day supply with no refills, and a healthcare facility that distributes the controlled substances for the purpose of administration in the licensed healthcare facility.
3. The data elements that must be reported to the PDMP by the dispenser include:
   a. Prescriber name and DEA number;
   b. Date the prescription was written and dispensed;
   c. Patient name, address, and birthdate;
   d. The NDC number of the drug dispensed;
   e. The quantity and days' supply of the drug dispensed;
   f. The NPI and DEA number of the dispenser or pharmacy; and
   g. Method of payment for the prescription.

STUDY TIP: This information is reported electronically, but for purposes of the MPJE you should know what is required to be reported and when it is required to be reported.

D. Mandatory Education and Continuing Education
   1. The ABC-MAP law/program requires all prescribers and dispensers to obtain mandatory education for licensure and mandatory continuing education for licensure renewal.
   2. To apply for licensure, 4 hours of Board-approved education consisting of 2 hours in pain management and 2 hours in the practice of prescribing or dispensing opioids. For license renewal, pharmacists are required to complete at least 2 hours of CE on the same topics, and these hours will count towards the total renewal CE requirements.

CHAPTER THREE

Pennsylvania Laws—Part 1
Overview, Prescriptive Authority,
Board of Pharmacy, Definitions,
Licensure, and the Pennsylvania Drugs,
Devices and Cosmetics Program

CHAPTER THREE
Pennsylvania Laws—Part 1
Overview, Prescriptive Authority, Board of Pharmacy, Definitions, Licensure, and the Pennsylvania Drugs, Devices and Cosmetics Program

I. **Pennsylvania Laws Impacting Pharmacy Practice**

This book does not cover every law and rule governing the practice of pharmacy in Pennsylvania, but instead highlights those most applicable to the MPJE Competency Statements. Rather than reviewing the laws and rules in order, this book, where possible, groups statutes and rules by topic. For most topics, a reference is provided to the specific statute or rule. This book summarizes and explains those provisions but may not always include the entire statutory or rule language. Often, the statutory or rule language is annotated to make it easier to understand, and the "notes" provide further explanation. The reader is advised to read all the laws and rules that apply in Pennsylvania.

The following are the most important provisions of Pennsylvania laws and rules relating to the practice of pharmacy.

A. Statutes (Laws)
   1. Pennsylvania Pharmacy Act (PPA) (63 P. S. §§ 390-1–390-13)
   2. Pennsylvania Controlled Substance, Drug, Device, and Cosmetic Act (PCSDDCA) (35 P. S. §§ 780-101–780.144)
   Note: This law primarily applies to manufacturers and distributors, although some provisions do apply to pharmacies.
   3. Pennsylvania Generic Equivalent Drug Law (35 P. S. §§ 960.1–960.7)
B. Rules—Pennsylvania Administrative Code
   1. Board of Pharmacy Rules and Regulations (49 Pa. Code §§ 27.1–27.606)
   2. Pennsylvania Controlled Substance, Drug, Device and Cosmetic Regulations (28 Pa. Code §§ 25.1–25.131)
   3. Pennsylvania Drug Equivalency Regulations (28 Pa. Code §§ 25.53–25.55)
   4. Pennsylvania Hospital Pharmacy Regulations (28 Pa. Code § 113)
   5. Pennsylvania Long-Term Care Nursing Facilities Regulations (28 Pa. Code § 211)

C. Additional Helpful Information
   1. The Pennsylvania Board of Pharmacy website (*https:// www.dos.pa.gov/ProfessionalLicensing/BoardsCommissions /Pharmacy/Pages/default.asp*) contains useful information for both practicing pharmacists and those seeking licensure in Pennsylvania. The website includes links to the Pennsylvania Pharmacy Act and Board of Pharmacy Rules and Regulations. This website *does not* contain readily available links to the additional Pennsylvania laws and rules listed and reviewed in this text.
   2. The most current information from the Pennsylvania Board of Pharmacy can be obtained from the main page and from the links provided under "Board Resources."
   3. Information on Board meetings and minutes are also provided on the Board website.
   4. Additional study resources and links are available on the Pennsylvania Department of Health website. For dispensers (pharmacies/pharmacists), this includes links to guides and FAQs regarding the electronic prescribing of controlled substances, naloxone dispensing and standing orders, the state PDMP, and prescribing and dispensing guidelines for opioids. Also, since businesses in Pennsylvania that manufacture and/or distribute retail drugs have to register with the Pennsylvania Department of Health, links to many of the state laws, rules, and guidance surrounding the Drugs, Devices and Cosmetics Program are available from the Department of Health website (*https://www.health.pa .gov/topics/programs/Pages/Drugs-Devices-and-Cosmetics .aspx*).

II. Prescriptive Authority and Scope of Practice
A. Prescriptive Authority
   1. Practitioners with Independent Authority. *See Chapter 2, Section VI. B*
      a. Allopathic physicians (M.D.) licensed under the Medical Practice Act
      b. Osteopathic physicians (D.O.) licensed under the Osteopathic Medical Practice Act
      c. Dentists licensed under the Dental Law
      d. Podiatrists licensed under the Podiatry Act

    e. Certified optometrists licensed under the Optometric Practice and Licensure Act

    f. Veterinarians licensed under the Veterinary Practice Act

2. Physician Assistants—Dependent Prescriptive Authority (49 Pa. Code §§ 18.121–18.183 and 49 Pa. Code §§ 25.141–25.201)

    a. A supervising physician may delegate to a physician assistant the prescribing or dispensing of medications. The supervising physician and physician assistant must have a written agreement that details their prescribing and dispensing authority. The pharmacist can request access to and confirm the physician assistant's authority to prescribe. The written agreement must list the categories of drugs the physician assistant is not permitted to prescribe.

    b. Prescription blanks:

        (1) Prescription blanks must have the name and license number of the physician assistant in a printed format at the heading of the blank. The supervising physician must also be identified.

        (2) The signature of the physician assistant must be followed by the initials "PA-C" or similar to identify the signer as a physician assistant. When required, the physician assistant's DEA number must appear on the prescriptions.

        (3) The supervising physician is prohibited from pre-signing prescription blanks.

    c. Controlled substance restrictions:

        (1) Schedule II controlled substances are limited to a 72-hour dose for initial therapy and a 30-day supply for ongoing therapy. The prescription must clearly state on its face that it is for initial or ongoing therapy.

        (2) Other restrictions on prescribing Schedule II opioids for pain are also applicable. *See Chapter 2, Section VII*

3. Certified Registered Nurse Practitioners (CRNPs)—Dependent Prescriptive Authority (49 Pa. Code §§ 21.251–21.377)

    a. A CRNP must have prescriptive authority from the Board of Nursing and enter into a collaborative written agreement with a supervising physician. A CRNP with prescriptive authority may prescribe and dispense drugs consistent with the collaborative agreement and relevant to the CRNP's specialty. A pharmacist can request to access the agreement. The Board of Nursing adopts the American Hospital Formulary Service Pharmacologic-Therapeutic classification to identify drugs that a CRNP may prescribe and dispense if authorized by the collaborative agreement. Prescriptions ordered by a CRNP must bear their name, title, and CRNP certification number and, when required, their DEA number.

   b. Controlled substance restrictions:

      (1) Schedule II controlled substances are limited to a 30-day supply as identified in a collaborative agreement.

      (2) Schedule III or IV controlled substances can be prescribed up to a 90-day supply as identified in the collaborative agreement.

      (3) A CRNP may not prescribe controlled substances in a pain management clinic.

      (4) A CRNP may prescribe an oral emergency prescription for a CII and a written prescription must be delivered to the pharmacist within 72 hours.

      (5) Other restrictions on prescribing Schedule II opioids for pain are also applicable. *See Chapter 2, Section VII*

4. Nurse Midwives (CNM)—Dependent Prescriptive Authority (49 Pa. Code §§ 18.1–18.9)

   a. A CNM must have prescriptive authority from the Board and enter into a collaborative written agreement with a supervising physician. A CNM with prescriptive authority may prescribe and dispense drugs consistent with the collaborative agreement. A pharmacist can request to access the agreement. Prescriptions ordered by a CNM must bear their name, title, contact information, and the initials "CNM," and, when required, their DEA number.

   b. A CNM may only prescribe a controlled substance for a woman's acute pain. CII prescriptions are limited to a 72-hour supply and may only be extended with the approval of the collaborating physician. CIII and CIV medications are limited to a 30-day supply and shall only be refilled with the approval of the collaborating physician.

   c. A CNM may only prescribe psychotropic drugs after consulting with the collaborating physician.

5. Certified Optometrists—Independent Authority but Limited Formulary
   a. Certified optometrists may administer and prescribe pharmaceutical agents for therapeutic purposes and to treat glaucoma. A list (formulary) of allowable pharmaceutical products is provided on the Board of Optometry's website (*https://www.dos.pa.gov/Professional Licensing/BoardsCommissions/Optometry/Documents /Special%20Notices/OptoSN%20-%20POA-Drugs %20Approved%20for%20PA%20Optometrists.pdf*). Optometrists that plan to prescribe or administer controlled substances must obtain their DEA number.
   b. The state formulary contains a list of topical anesthetics, topical ocular lubricants, topical ophthalmic dyes and stains, topical hyperosmotic agents, topical autonomic drugs, topical NSAIDs, oral and topical antibiotic agents, topical antifungal and antiparasitic agents, oral and topical antivirals, oral analgesic drugs, topical anti-allergy drugs, oral and topical steroids, topical immunomodulators, and oral and topical glaucoma agents. The oral analgesic drugs are limited to codeine in combination with acetaminophen or aspirin, hydrocodone in combination with acetaminophen or ibuprofen (not to exceed a 72-hour supply), pentazocine, and tramadol.
B. Miscellaneous Prescriptive Authority Issues
   1. Scope of Practice
      a. A physician (D.O. or M.D.) may legally prescribe a drug to treat any disease or illness. Although a pharmacist should exercise caution, it is legal to fill a prescription written outside of a physician's specialty, such as a hypertension medication written by an orthopedic surgeon or an oncologist.
      b. Dentists, podiatrists, and veterinarians may only prescribe drugs used within their scope of practice. For example, a veterinarian cannot prescribe drugs for humans, and a prescription from a dentist for birth control pills would not be a valid prescription.
      c. Prescriptive authority for certified optometrists is restricted to the approved formulary.
      d. While many states do permit pharmacists to order or prescribe limited medicinal drugs in specific

circumstances, Pennsylvania does not currently grant prescriptive authority to pharmacists.

2. Self-Prescribing and Prescribing for Family Members
   a. According to the American Medical Association, physicians generally should not treat themselves or members of their immediate family. In emergency situations or isolated settings where there is no other qualified physician available, a physician could treat themselves or family members until another physician becomes available. There are also situations that involve short-term, minor problems where care of themselves or family members is acceptable. Regarding the prescribing of controlled substances, except in emergencies, it is not appropriate for physicians to write prescriptions for themselves or family members.
   b. Prescribing drugs must be done in good faith in the course of professional practice, within the scope of the patient relationship, and in accordance with accepted treatment principles.
   c. Pharmacists could be disciplined for dispensing drugs when the pharmacist knows or has reason to believe a purported prescription is not based on a valid practitioner-patient relationship.

STUDY TIP: Even without a specific law that prohibits self-prescribing or prescribing for family members, pharmacists should exercise caution and only fill such prescriptions if they can validate that there is a valid practitioner-patient relationship and that the prescription was issued in the usual course of practice.

---

3. Retired or Deceased Practitioners
   a. One of the MPJE Competency Statements includes how to handle prescriptions after a practitioner retires or dies.
   b. The PBOP Rules provide that no prescription may be knowingly filled or refilled for a patient whose prescription was written for prior use by a prescriber who is deceased or no longer in practice. *See 49 Pa. Code § 27.18(h)*

STUDY TIP: Remember that a pharmacist is not permitted to fill or refill prescriptions when the prescriber is deceased or no longer in practice. Since the PBOP regulations state that in these situations you can't fill, this is how you should answer. This may not be a satisfactory choice for the patient, but it is the best legal answer.

---

4. Approved Drugs for Unapproved Uses—Off-Label Use
    a. There is no law that prohibits a practitioner from prescribing, or a pharmacist from dispensing, an approved drug for a use that is not approved in the drug's labeling.
    b. Pharmacists should use their professional judgment in these situations and consider liability implications.
5. Office Use Prescriptions
    a. Except for specific situations (such as dispensing naloxone based on a non-patient-specific standing order), medicinal drugs can only be dispensed based on a patient-specific prescription.
    b. A prescription written "For Office Use" cannot be filled. A pharmacist can sell an original manufacturer's bottle of a prescription drug to a practitioner for use in his or her office, but cannot dispense drugs pursuant to a prescription for "office use."

III. Pennsylvania Board of Pharmacy (63 P. S. § 390-6)
A. Purpose
    1. The Pennsylvania Board of Pharmacy (PBOP) was established by the legislature to ensure that every pharmacist practicing in this state and every pharmacy meet minimum requirements for safe practice.
    2. The PBOP is responsible for the licensure of pharmacy professionals and pharmacies. The PBOP also has the power to regulate the practice of pharmacy in Pennsylvania.

STUDY TIP: Remember, the purpose of the Board of Pharmacy is to protect the public health, safety, and welfare. The Board of Pharmacy is not responsible for advocating for pharmacists or pharmacies.

B. Organization
    1. The PBOP is one of many regulatory boards under the Pennsylvania Department of State. It is composed of 9 members.
    2. Five members must be licensed pharmacists who are residents of Pennsylvania and who have been licensed pharmacists in Pennsylvania for at least 5 years. 2 members are consumer/public-at-large members. The other 2 members consist of the Commissioner of Professional and Occupational Affairs and the Director of the Bureau of Consumer Protection in the Office of the Attorney General.

    3. The pharmacist members must include:
        a. 2 pharmacists from independent retail pharmacies;
        b. 2 pharmacists that are employed by retail chain pharmacies which operate 5 or more pharmacies in Pennsylvania; and
        c. The remaining 1 pharmacist shall be from an acute care institutional pharmacy.

C. Appointment and Terms
    1. Board of Pharmacy members are appointed by the Governor and confirmed by the Pennsylvania Senate.
    2. Board members are appointed for 6-year terms; however, if a Board member's term ends, they may continue to serve until a new Board member has been appointed, but no longer than 6 months beyond the 6-year period.
    3. A Board member may not serve more than 2 consecutive terms.

    Note: The Board is run by an Executive Director. The Executive Director is an employee of the state. The Executive Director is not one of the 9 Board of Pharmacy members but does have to be a pharmacist.

IV. Definitions

STUDY TIP: Definitions are often the key to understanding legal topics and answering legal questions. Always be sure to read the definition section of a statute or rule carefully. In addition, Pennsylvania statutory definitions often contain definitions within definitions and sometimes place specific requirements on pharmacists and pharmacies directly in the definitions rather than in a separate section. For all these reasons, it is imperative to read and understand definitions. Some of the most important definitions from the Pennsylvania Pharmacy Act (PPA) and Pennsylvania Board of Pharmacy (PBOP) Rules and Regulations are provided below.

A. Dispense or dispensing—the preparation of a prescription or nonprescription drug in a suitable container appropriately labeled for subsequent administration to or use by a patient or other individual entitled to receive the drug.

B. Non-proprietary drug—a drug containing any quantity of any controlled substance or any drug which is required by any applicable Federal or State law to be dispensed only by prescription.

C. Proprietary drug—nonprescription, non-narcotic medicines or drugs which may be sold without a prescription and which are prepackaged for use by the consumer and labeled in accordance with the requirements of the statutes and regulations of this state and the federal government.

D. Prescription—a written or oral order issued by a duly licensed medical practitioner in the course of his or her professional practice for a controlled substance, other drug or device, or medication which is dispensed for use by a consumer.

E. Emergency prescription—a refill of a prescription which is essential to the continuation of therapy in a chronic condition, for which the refill has not been authorized and for which the pharmacist notifies the prescriber within 72 hours that an emergency prescription has been dispensed.

Note: This is an example of the Pennsylvania law placing mandatory requirements in the definition section of the law. There are additional requirements for emergency prescriptions found within the text of the PPA as well.

F. Pharmacist—an individual duly licensed by the State Board of Pharmacy to engage in the practice of pharmacy.

G. Practice of Pharmacy—the provision of healthcare services by a pharmacist, which includes:

1. The interpretation, evaluation, and implementation of medical orders for the provision of pharmacy services or prescription drug orders;
2. the delivery, dispensing, or distribution of prescription drugs;
3. participation in drug and device selection;
4. drug administration;
5. drug regimen review;
6. drug or drug-related research;
7. compounding;
8. proper and safe storage of drugs and devices;
9. management of drug therapy under a written collaborative agreement (as set forth in the Pharmacy Act), or if in an institutional setting, consistent with the institution's assignment of clinical duties under a written agreement or protocol (as set forth in the PPA);
10. maintaining proper records;
11. patient counseling;

12. acts, services, operations, or transactions necessary or incident to the provision of these healthcare services; and
13. drug therapy management, including services provided under the Medicare Prescription Drug, Improvement, and Modernization Act of 2003.
14. The "practice of pharmacy" does not include the operations of a manufacturer or distributor as defined in the PCSDDCA.

H. Management of drug therapy—any of the following processes performed under a written protocol or collaborative agreement (as set forth in the PPA):
1. adjusting a drug regimen;
2. adjusting drug strength, frequency of administration, or route;
3. administration of drugs;
4. ordering of laboratory tests and ordering or performing other diagnostic tests necessary in the management of drug therapy;
5. monitoring the patient's vital signs; and
6. providing education and training to the patient, which is related to the management of drug therapy.
   Note: Pennsylvania allows the management of drug therapy under different sections of the PPA and PBOP Rules. Each section pertains to a different practice setting. The reason for this is because the management of drug therapy was only initially permitted in institutions, but it was later expanded to additional practice sites.

I. Drug administration—the direct introduction of or the application of a drug into or on the body of a patient by injection, inhalation, ingestion, or any other means and, where required by law, shall occur only pursuant to a medical order.
Note: Under the definition of "Practice of Pharmacy," Pennsylvania allows the administration of drugs. The definition of "drug administration" extends beyond injection of immunizations.

J. Protocol—a written document that describes the nature and scope of the drug therapy management to be carried out by the pharmacist.

K. Nonresident pharmacy—any pharmacy located outside this Commonwealth that ships, mails, or delivers, in any manner, legend devices or legend drugs into this Commonwealth pursuant to a prescription order.

V. Licensure of Individuals

A. Licensure of Pharmacists

1. Licensure by examination (63 P. S. § 390-3 and PBOP Rule 49 Pa. Code § 27.21)

a. Complete the online application (via PALS, the Pennsylvania Licensing System) and pay the required fees.

b. Must be at least 21 years of age.

c. Must have received a degree from an ACPE accredited school or college of pharmacy; or, if a graduate from a foreign pharmacy school not accredited by ACPE, must also pass the Foreign Pharmacy Graduate Equivalency Exam (FPGEE). To sit for the FPGEE, one must first show proficiency in the English language. The Board may make exceptions for foreign graduate requirements on a case-by-case basis. *See PBOP Rule 49 Pa. Code § 27.52*

d. Must submit proof of completion of internship program approved by the Board where the intern served at least 1,500 hours.
Note: PBOP Rule 49 Pa. Code § 27.26 states that 1,000 of the 1,500 hours can be earned from pharmacy school internships/rotations, with the remaining 500 hours to be earned by the intern outside of the school's program. However, the PBOP is currently waiving this requirement and allowing all 1,500 hours to be earned through pharmacy school rotations. (See PBOP's website for the announcement. This requirement is not waived for foreign pharmacy school graduates, who must still complete 1,500 hours, with at least 500 hours outside of a school program and in a licensed pharmacy.)

e. Has not been convicted of a felony related to controlled substances unless at least 10 years have passed and the applicant demonstrates to the PBOP that they are not a risk to the public.

f. Must pass the North American Pharmacist Licensure Examination (NAPLEX) and the Pennsylvania Multistate Pharmacy Jurisprudence Exam (MPJE).

2. Additional Information on Licensure by Examination

a. Information on a submitted application is valid for 6 months and then must be updated. An entirely new application and fee are required once the application is 1 year old.

b. All health-related licenses in Pennsylvania are mandatory reporters of child abuse. Anyone applying for an initial pharmacist license must complete 3 hours of approved training by the Pennsylvania State Department of Human Services (DHS). DHS will then submit the completed course to the Pennsylvania Bureau of Professional and Occupational Affairs. *See PA Act 31 of 2014*

c. Anyone applying for initial licensure as a pharmacist must complete at least 4 hours of Board-approved education consisting of 2 hours in pain management and 2 hours in the practice of prescribing or dispensing of opioids. Pharmacist applicants must document within 1 year from issuance of the license to practice pharmacy that they completed this education. Alternatively, if the applicant completed this education as part of their pharmacy school curriculum, the applicant can request their pharmacy school to complete and directly submit to the Board the verification of opioid education form posted on the Board's website. Otherwise, the applicant can complete ACPE accredited programs.

3. Licensure by reciprocity (63 P. S. § 390-3 and PBOP Rule 49 Pa. Code § 27.25)

Note: Other states may use the terms "endorsement" or "license transfer."

a. Must meet age, internship, and education requirements listed above in 1b., 1c., and 1d. As an alternative to showing completion of 1,500 intern hours, applicants can show work as a pharmacist in another state for at least 1 year.

b. Must have obtained a passing score on NAPLEX and submit evidence of active pharmacist licensure in another state.

c. Must submit online application and pay any required fees. Information on application is valid for 6 months, and application expires 1 year from when it was processed.

d. Must obtain a passing score on the Pennsylvania MPJE. The MPJE is not required if the applicant obtained an initial pharmacist license after 1983 and passed the Federal Drug Law Examination (FDLE) for the license that is being transferred.

    e. Complete the required state-approved 3 hours of child abuse education and 4 hours of opioid education as described under 2.b. and 2.c. above.

    f. Prior discipline by another state board and/or a past criminal conviction could impact obtaining a Pennsylvania pharmacist license. An applicant will be required to provide further details regarding the situation on their application.

4. Additional Information Regarding Pharmacist Licensure

    a. The PPA still has language within it requiring a pharmacist applicant to have "good moral character." A newer Pennsylvania state law was passed (PA Act 53 of 2020) that prohibits state licensing boards from denying licensure based on "good moral character."

    b. Act 53 also required a Best Practices Guide to be established that is to be used by applicants to understand how the use of criminal convictions can be used in professional licensing determinations.

    c. Act 53 requires each board to develop and publish a schedule of criminal offenses that may constitute grounds to deny, suspend, or revoke a license.

    d. Act 53 also provides for a process for individuals that have a criminal conviction to request a preliminary determination as to whether a particular conviction will bar licensure.

    e. For more information about Act 53, please see the PBOP website or go to *https://www.dos.pa.gov/Professional Licensing/Documents/ACT-53-Best-Practices-Guide.pdf.*

5. Renewal of Pharmacist License (63 P. S. § 390-3; 63 P. S. § 390-3.2; PBOP Rule 49 Pa. Code § 27.31)

    a. Must submit renewal application online, pay fee, and comply with continuing education requirements. *See details for continuing education requirements in B. below.*

    b. Licenses renew biennially (every 2 years) and expire on September 30th of even-numbered years.

    c. Renewal information will be provided 45–60 days in advance; late renewals are not permitted and will require submission of a reactivation license application.

    d. If a renewal is desired but the pharmacist has let their license lapse for more than 1 year, in addition to completing the renewal application, the pharmacist will also

have to apply to reactivate their license and show current proficiency in the practice of pharmacy. This will be met if the pharmacist was actively practicing as a full-time pharmacist in a different state while the Pennsylvania license was lapsed or through completion of CE.
Note: A pharmacist allowing their license to lapse may so notify the Board on the renewal form. Reasons shall be briefly stated, and the pharmacist's pocket license and display license shall be surrendered to the Board with the renewal form.

e. Any licensed pharmacist in Pennsylvania who is also licensed to practice pharmacy in any other state must report this information on their biennial registration renewal application. Any disciplinary action taken by another state must be reported on the renewal application or within 30 days of the final outcome, whichever is earlier.

STUDY TIP: The PPA states 90 days of the final outcome, but there is a separate state law (PA Act 6 of 2018) that requires 30 days. Therefore, follow the stricter law.

B. Continuing Education (CE) Requirements (63 P. S. § 390-3.1; 63 P. S. § 390-9.2; PBOP Rule 49 Pa. Code § 27.321)

1. To renew a pharmacist license, a pharmacist must obtain 30 hours of continuing education in courses approved by the Board during the preceding biennial renewal period (24 months prior to expiration of the license). Excess CE earned in one renewal period cannot be carried over into the next renewal period.

2. Pharmacists, for renewal, must complete 2 hours of an ACPE course with the topic designator of "Patient Safety." The ACPE "Patient Safety" program will be in the format ___-____-__-___-_05-P. These hours will count towards the required 30 hours of CE.

3. Pharmacists, for renewal, must complete 2 hours of ACPE-approved CE on pain management or the identification of addiction, or on the prescribing and dispensing of opioids. Although this requirement comes from a different state law (PA Act 124 of 2016), the pharmacist must still obtain ACPE

pharmacy-approved CE programs on these topics; therefore, the SBOP will count these 2 hours as part of the required 30 hours of CE.

Note: For initial pharmacist licensure, the requirement is 4 hours, but for renewal it is 2 hours.

4. Pharmacists, for renewal, must complete 2 hours of a Board-approved child abuse recognition and reporting requirements education program. Although this requirement comes from a different state law (PA Act 31 of 2014), the PBOP will count these 2 hours as part of the required 30 hours of CE.

Note: For initial licensure, the requirement is 3 hours for child abuse education, but for renewal it is 2 hours. Since the child abuse recognition and reporting CE programs are approved by the PBOP and not by ACPE, this CE falls outside of the normal channels and recordkeeping of ACPE-approved pharmacist CE courses. Pharmacists can review and check the status of ACPE-approved pharmacist CE on the NABP CPE Monitor; however, information on completed child abuse programs is unavailable on the CPE Monitor.

5. Both live and correspondence courses will be accepted by the PBOP as long as they are offered by approved providers. The PBOP accepts ACPE-accredited programs. For non-ACPE-accredited programs, the provider must obtain prior approval from the PBOP.

STUDY TIP: Do not get mixed up between continuing education hours and continuing education units. Nearly everyone tracks CE by hours, but ACPE tracks continuing education units, or CEUs, which means a 1-hour CE course will be accredited as 0.1 CEUs. If you see an ACPE course accredited as 0.3 CEUs, that equals 3 CE hours.

---

6. A pharmacist licensed and authorized to administer injectable medications, biologicals, and immunizations must complete at least 2 hours of the required 30 hours of CE on these topics to renew their license. This includes topics that concern the administration of injectable medications, biologicals, and immunizations, including, but not limited to, disease epidemiology, vaccine characteristics, injection technique, emergency response to adverse events, and related topics.

7. Initial Renewal and Prorating of CEs
   a. Pharmacists who applied by examination and are renewing their licenses for the first time are exempt from completing the regular pharmacist CE for the first renewal, but must still complete a Board-approved child abuse continuing education program as well as the required CEs on opioids/pain management in order to renew their licenses.
   b. Pharmacists who applied by reciprocity and are renewing their licenses for the first time will have their continuing education prorated for their first renewal period only. CEs are prorated based on a quarterly basis from the date of licensure to the next date of renewal. Each quarter licensed will consist of 3 months and will require the pharmacist to obtain 3.75 CE hours. The additional CE requirements (patient safety, the authorization to administer injectable medications, biologicals and immunizations, child abuse recognition and reporting, and pain management/opioids) still apply even if the pharmacist must complete less than 30 contact hours for the first renewal.
8. A pharmacist whose license has been suspended or revoked for disciplinary reasons must comply with CE requirements during the period of suspension or revocation, if the pharmacist wants to resume practice or petition for licensure reinstatement at the conclusion of the disciplinary period.
9. The PBOP audits CE requirements. Pharmacists not meeting CE requirements or fraudulently reporting CE requirements will be disciplined. In addition, a pharmacist will have 6 months from the notice of deficiency to make up delinquent CE hours. *See PBOP Rule 49 Pa. Code § 27.32(b)*
10. Tracking Continuing Education
    a. NABP has an online CE tracking service called CPE Monitor, and all ACPE-approved providers report CE hours to CPE Monitor. There are additional programs, one being CE Broker, which some states require to be used for tracking of CEs.
    b. The PBOP has reminded pharmacists that non-ACPE programs approved by the Board (e.g., Pennsylvania-approved child abuse programs) are not tracked in CPE monitor.

PHARMACIST CONTINUING EDUCATION REQUIREMENTS

	Renewal License	Initial License (New Graduate)	Initial License (Reciprocity)
Licensure Time Frame[1]	2 years	Varies	Varies
Number of CE Hours Required by Board of Pharmacy Rules	30	Board CE waived for initial licensure period	Prorated to 3.75 for each full quarter during initial licensure[2]
Number of CE Hours Required in Patient Safety[3]	2 (Counts toward 30)	Waived for initial licensure period	2 during initial licensure period
Number of CE Hours Required in Immunization Topics[4]	2 (Counts toward 30)	Waived for initial licensure period	2 during initial licensure period
Number of Hours Required in Child Abuse Recognition and Reporting[5,6]	2 (Counts toward 30)	3 as a condition of initial licensure and 2 for every biennial renewal	3 as a condition for initial licensure and 2 for every biennial renewal
Number of Hours Required in Opioid Practices[5,7]	2 (Counts toward 30)	4 with initial licensure and 2 for every biennial renewal	4 with initial licensure and 2 for every biennial renewal

1. Licensure period for renewing pharmacists is 2 years (Oct. 1–Sept. 30 of even-numbered years). Initial licensure time frames will vary as issuance dates differ, but expiration date is fixed.

2. Reciprocating pharmacists must complete all topic-specific CEs listed, even if the number of prorated hours is fewer than the specific topic requirements.

3. Must be ACPE Topic Designator "Patient Safety" which is "05."

4. Only required if individual is authorized to immunize.

5. Board cannot waive this requirement as the mandate is based on different state law.

6. Programs must be approved by the PBOP.

7. "Opioid Practices" includes education in pain management, addiction, and prescribing and dispensing practices for opioids. 4 hours of education is required with initial licensure, but the individual has 12 months to submit accepted documentation of the education, including hours from pharmacy school curriculum or ACPE-approved programs.

C. License for Authorization to Administer Injectables for Pharmacist (63 P. S. § 390-9.2; PBOP Rules 49 Pa. Code §§ 27.401–27.407)

    1. A license for authorization to administer injectables is an additional voluntary license that a registered Pennsylvania pharmacist may apply for and obtain through the PBOP.

    2. Requirements:

        a. Must hold an active license to practice pharmacy in Pennsylvania.

        b. Must have completed a PBOP-approved course of education and training. The PBOP approves courses offered by

ACPE-accredited providers and educational institutions that meet the PBOP criteria and provide instruction on the topics listed in the PBOP rules.

c. The PBOP allows an applicant to directly submit a certificate from the American Pharmacists Association's Pharmacy-Based Immunization Delivery certificate program. For other completed certificate programs, the provider of the program must submit the required forms to the PBOP. An injectables training program is valid for only two years from the date of completion.
Note: At the time of publication of this book, the Board had proposed changes to PBOP Rule 49 Pa. Code § 27.407(a)(1) to allow the training program to be valid for 3 years from the date of completion. Please verify the PBOP Rule prior to taking the exam to determine the most current information.

d. Must be CPR certified by a PBOP-approved organization (e.g., American Heart Association or American Red Cross).

e. Must carry professional liability insurance in the minimum amount of 1 million dollars per occurrence or claims made. Failure to maintain coverage will lead to discipline. The PBOP accepts proof of personally purchased liability insurance or coverage provided by the pharmacist's employer.

f. Must renew license for authorization every 2 years (by September 30 of even-numbered years) and complete 2 hours of related CE. Late renewals will not be accepted, and an application to reactivate the license must be submitted.

3. Conditions and Authority for Administration

a. A pharmacist who is granted authority may administer injectable medications, biologicals, and immunizations to persons who are more than 18 years of age. The PBOP defines a person as more than 18 years of age on the day following the person's 18th birthday. Pharmacists are also permitted to administer influenza immunizations by injectable or needle-free delivery methods to persons 9 years of age and older. For individuals under 18 years of age, parental consent must be obtained prior to administration.

b. A pharmacist must administer injectable immunizations in accordance with treatment guidelines established by the Centers for Disease Control and Prevention (CDC) and which have been approved by the PBOP.

c. A pharmacist authorized by the PBOP to administer injectable medications, biologicals, and immunizations may only do so under either an order or written protocol.

    (1) The order from a licensed prescriber must be written, received electronically, or, if received orally, be reduced to writing and contain at a minimum:

        (i) the identity of the prescriber, patient, and the medication, immunization, or vaccine to be administered;

        (ii) the dose to be administered;

        (iii) the date of the original order and, if applicable, the schedule of subsequent administration.

    (2) Written protocols entered into between pharmacies/pharmacists and physicians/institutions may be valid for up to 2 years and must include the following:

        (i) the identity of the parties of the agreement;

        (ii) the identity of the medication, biological, or immunization which may be administered and the route of administration;

        (iii) the identity of the patient or groups of patients that can receive the product;

        (iv) a provision detailing instructions on how the pharmacist should address emergency situations such as adverse reactions;

        (v) recordkeeping requirements and notification of administration; and

        (vi) a provision allowing for termination of the protocol at the request of any party at any time.

4. Recordkeeping and Notification Requirements
   a. Records of each administration must be maintained for at least 2 years. Records must include:
      (1) patient name, address, and date of birth;
      (2) date of administration and injection site;
      (3) name, dose, manufacturer, lot number, and expiration date of the product administered;
      (4) the patient's primary care provider (if known);
      (5) the identity of the administering pharmacist;
      (6) documentation of informed consent;
      (7) the nature of the adverse event and who was notified, if applicable; and
      (8) the VIS statement, the date of the VIS statement, and the date and to whom the VIS statement was provided.
   b. Administration under an order requires notification to the prescriber as soon as possible, but no longer than 72 hours after administration. Administration under a written protocol requires notification of administration to the protocol physician within 72 hours and to the patient's primary care provider, if known, within 48 hours of administration.

   Note: At the time of publication, the PBOP Rule (49 Pa. Code § 27.406) required notification within 72 hours to the prescribing or protocol physician. This time frame is currently in the process of being amended and is expected to change to requiring notification to the prescribing or protocol physician within 48 hours. The additional 48-hour requirement to notify the patient's primary care provider, if known, is currently only found in the PPA, but it will also be included in the PBOP Rules once amended. Prior to taking the MPJE, please verify if the 72-hour time frame is still active or whether the proposed amendment has been finalized to the expected 48-hour time frame. The MPJE will test the current information at the time the test is taken.

   c. Notification is to include the identity of the patient and the product administered, the route of administration, the site of administration, the dose administered, and the date of administration.

d. In the event of any adverse event or reaction experienced by the patient either under an order or a written protocol, the pharmacist shall notify the patient's physician as soon as is practicable, and in no event later than 24 hours after learning of the adverse event or reaction. *Note: Be aware that for an adverse event, it is the patient's physician that is to be notified, even when under written protocol. The prescriber for the written protocol will likely be different than the patient's physician.*

5. Expected Rule Amendment
Now with the PPA amended to allow authorized pharmacists to delegate authorized interns to immunize, a proposed rule will be added that will prohibit pharmacists supervising interns immunizing if the pharmacist fails to carry professional liability insurance. (Expected PBOP Rule 49 Pa. Code § 27.408.)

D. Registration of Pharmacy Interns (63 P. S. § 390-3(e); PBOP Rule 49 Pa. Code § 27.26)

1. Pharmacy interns in the state must be registered by the PBOP prior to receiving any internship credit. Registration as a pharmacy intern is required for students attending pharmacy schools inside or outside of Pennsylvania and completing school rotations in Pennsylvania, or for students or graduates that will be earning intern hours outside of a school program in a Pennsylvania pharmacy.

2. Registration as a pharmacy intern will be available to an individual who has completed at least 2 years of college and is enrolled or accepted as a student of pharmacy in an ACPE-accredited pharmacy degree program.

3. An intern may not perform any acts related to the practice of pharmacy unless it is done under the direct and immediate personal supervision of a licensed pharmacist.

4. A pharmacy intern registration is valid for 6 years from the date it was issued. Any time spent in the military while registered is excluded from this time limit. Once a pharmacy intern receives their Pennsylvania pharmacist's license, the intern registration terminates. A pharmacy intern registration will also automatically become invalid if the pharmacy intern is no longer enrolled in pharmacy school, and the registration must be returned to the PBOP.

5. The PBOP will not approve internship hours for an intern when the supervising pharmacist was not registered as a preceptor unless the internship hours were acquired in an internship program sponsored or approved by an ACPE-accredited pharmacy school. The PBOP will also only grant internship credit for activities related to the practice of pharmacy.

6. Pharmacies and pharmacists that train and precept interns must meet certain requirements.
   a. A pharmacy cannot have been or be in violation of any laws or rules governing the practice of pharmacy in which it is engaged. A pharmacy may appeal to the PBOP for a waiver of this.
   b. A pharmacy shall compound and dispense a sufficient number of prescriptions to provide the intern with ample opportunity to scrutinize prescriptions and to compound and dispense under the supervision of a licensed pharmacist.
   c. To register as an intern's preceptor, the pharmacist shall hold an unrestricted license and be engaged full-time in the active practice of pharmacy in Pennsylvania, as well as not have any past criminal convictions relating to the practice of pharmacy.
   d. A pharmacist preceptor may not direct the training of more than two pharmacy interns at any one time, unless the program has been approved by the PBOP for a greater number (for example, school-sponsored internship programs are not limited to 2 interns per preceptor).

7. A total of 1,500 hours of internship are required to become licensed as a pharmacist.
   a. Currently, the SBOP is accepting all 1,500 hours from an internship program sponsored by approved pharmacy schools. (The PBOP is waiving its rule that only allows 1,000 hours to be obtained through a pharmacy school program.)
   b. A maximum of 50 hours may be credited in 1 week.

8. To obtain a Pennsylvania pharmacy intern registration, the applicant must also complete the required state-approved 3 hours of child abuse education.

9. Pharmacists can allow registered pharmacy interns to immunize if the pharmacist is providing direct and

immediate supervision of the intern and the intern has obtained their own authority to immunize. To obtain authority, the registered pharmacy intern must apply to the PBOP through the PALS system, which also requires proof of CPR certification and completion of a PBOP-approved training program (e.g., APhA certification) within 2 years of application.

Note: At the time of publication of this book, the 2-year time frame was still valid, but proposed PBOP rules that included changing this time frame to 3 years were expected to be finalized. Please verify the most current information when preparing for the MPJE.

STUDY TIP: An intern does not need to enter into a protocol with a physician to provide immunizations but must be authorized to administer immunizations and be under the supervision of a pharmacist who is also authorized to administer immunizations.

E. Registration of Pharmacy Technicians (63 P. S. § 390-3.3)
   1. Until 2020, Pennsylvania did not have any legal requirement for pharmacy technicians to register with the state. PA Act 140 of 2020 amended the PPA to require registration of pharmacy technicians.
   2. The PBOP could take years to implement rules and regulations that define and detail technician registration requirements under PA Act 140 of 2020. Until this occurs, technicians are not required to meet any registration requirements in Pennsylvania.
   3. Once promulgated and finalized, future PBOP rules regarding pharmacy technicians will include the following:
      a. The PBOP will create rules that regulate "Pharmacy Technicians" and "Pharmacy Technician Trainees."
      b. An individual must be at least 17 years old and a high school graduate to register with the PBOP as a pharmacy technician, or 16 years old to become a pharmacy technician trainee.
      c. To apply to become a pharmacy technician, one must complete a PBOP-approved training program. While completing the training program in a licensed pharmacy, the individual will have to obtain a temporary permit from the PBOP as a pharmacy technician trainee.

d. Registration as a pharmacy technician will be required biennially. Registration will also allow the PBOP to discipline a registered pharmacy technician if needed.

F. Proof of License; Display of License (63 P. S. §§ 390-4(d), 390-5(9) (ix), (x); PBOP Rule 49 Pa. Code § 27.11(e))

   1. All licenses, registrations, and permits issued under the PPA shall be displayed in a conspicuous place in the licensed pharmacy. Therefore, every pharmacy, pharmacist, pharmacy intern, and registered pharmacy technician (once PBOP rules are finalized) must display the current document at the licensed pharmacy the entity or individual is affiliated with.

   2. A pharmacy is not permitted to display any license, registration, or permit for anyone that is not lawfully employed at the location it is displayed at.

   3. It is considered unprofessional conduct, and a reason for discipline, to display a pharmacist's license in a pharmacy which one is not the owner of or employed by. It is also unprofessional conduct, and a reason for discipline, if a pharmacist does not have his/her biennial pocket registration card available for inspection by an authorized agent when practicing. *Note: In addition to receiving a standard-sized license that can be framed and displayed in the pharmacy where a pharmacist practices, each pharmacist will also receive a pocket registration card. This card is to be kept with the pharmacist while practicing. This becomes especially important if a PBOP inspector requests the license information of a pharmacist who works at multiple locations (such as a floating pharmacist) and does not always display their license.*

VI. Pharmacy Permits

A. General Permit Requirements (63 P. S. § 390-4; PBOP Rules 49 Pa. Code §§ 27.11, 27.14, 27.31, 27.41, 27.42)

1. Prior to advertising a pharmacy or engaging in the operation of a pharmacy, a person or business entity must file an application and obtain a pharmacy permit from the PBOP.

    a. The application requires the full name and Pennsylvania pharmacist license number for the pharmacist who will be serving as the pharmacist manager/pharmacist in charge.

    b. A pharmacist may only be registered as the pharmacist manager/pharmacist in charge at only one pharmacy.

    c. The application also requires information on the pharmacy's ownership, including the type of ownership, the name of the pharmacy's direct owner, and information on the principal officers, administrators, and directors. Anyone that holds more than a 10% interest must be identified.

    d. If a medical practitioner has any proprietary or beneficial interest in the pharmacy, the percentage of interest along with a statement regarding their direction, control, and daily operation of the pharmacy is required.

2. An affidavit must be completed by the pharmacist manager and the pharmacy owner's authorized representative and included with the application. The affidavit requires confirmation that the proposed pharmacy will meet the requirements of the PPA and PBOP Regulations and that the individuals who operate that pharmacy will comply with PBOP policies and procedures.

3. Information on a submitted application is valid for 6 months and then must be updated. An entirely new application and fee are required once the application is 1 year old. Certain questions on the application (e.g., a legal question asking if applicant has any pending indictments, alleged violations, and/or convictions), if answered yes, will require detailed information to be uploaded for Board evaluation.

4. A detailed sketch showing the floor plan and information for the prescription area as well as the other areas of the pharmacy is required with the application. Failure to provide this information on the entire pharmacy may result in a delay in the processing of the application.

5. Once the application for a pharmacy permit is fully completed and the pharmacy is ready for inspection, a pharmacy inspector will schedule an inspection. A pharmacy permit will be issued only if the pharmacy application is complete and accurate, and the pharmacy has passed inspection.

6. A permit to conduct a pharmacy must show the name and address of the pharmacy, the name of the current owner, and the name of the current pharmacist manager.

7. A change in name or ownership or controlling interest in the pharmacy requires a new permit. An application for a new permit must be filed within 30 days of the change in name, ownership, or controlling interest.

8. A pharmacy that closes or ceases operation must immediately return the pharmacy permit to the PBOP and provide information on the location of the prescription files and nonproprietary drugs. After 30 days, prescription files or nonproprietary drugs may not be sold, transferred, or disposed of unless prior permission from the PBOP is obtained. When a pharmacy closes or ceases operations, any signs, symbols, or other indications of a pharmacy must be immediately removed from both the interior and exterior of the premises.

9. When a pharmacist manager ceases to hold that position, the pharmacy permit holder must inform the PBOP in writing of this and of the new pharmacist manager not more than 15 days later. If the PBOP does not object within 30 days of notification, the new pharmacist manager is considered approved. If the permit holder is unable to replace the pharmacist manager within those 15 days, the permit holder may request in writing an extension of up to 30 additional days to obtain a replacement. A pharmacy may not operate without a pharmacist manager for more than 15 days unless the pharmacy first obtains from the PBOP an extension of time for obtaining a replacement.
   Note: In Pennsylvania, it is the pharmacy owner/pharmacy permit holder's obligation to inform the Board of a change in pharmacist manager.

10. A pharmacist may not serve as the pharmacist manager of more than one pharmacy at any given time. When a pharmacy permit holder loses the services of a pharmacist manager and cannot obtain a replacement, it may apply in writing to the PBOP for a temporary waiver of this requirement,

and the PBOP may grant a waiver authorizing a pharmacist manager to serve as the pharmacist manager of more than one pharmacy for up to 60 days after the initial 15 days permitted to operate without a named pharmacist manager. *Note: While a pharmacy can go 15 days without a listed pharmacist manager and request an extension for another 30 days to find a replacement, another option is to request that a pharmacist manager of one location serve a second location for up to an additional 60 days past the initial 15 days without a pharmacist manager.*

11. Each pharmacy in Pennsylvania will require a separate permit regardless of ownership unless the pharmacy is a satellite pharmacy. The PBOP defines "satellite pharmacy" as a pharmacy in an institution which provides specialized services for the patients of the institution and which is dependent upon the centrally located pharmacy for administrative control, staffing, and drug procurement. Furthermore, the PBOP has provided that the term "satellite pharmacy" does not include a pharmacy serving the public on the premises of an institution, nor does it include a pharmacy located off premises from the centrally located pharmacy of the institution regardless of whether the pharmacy is owned by the same person or entity which owns the institution.

12. A pharmacy must always be under the constant direct and personal supervision and management of a Pennsylvania licensed pharmacist that does not supervise more than one pharmacy at the same time (unless waived by the PBOP).

13. The prescription area of a pharmacy can only be open when there is a licensed pharmacist on duty at all times. However, the PBOP permits a sole pharmacist on duty to take up to a 30-minute break while the pharmacy remains open if certain requirements are met. These include:

    a. The pharmacist shall remain in the pharmacy, or for a pharmacy that is located within a retail establishment or institution, in the immediate building containing the pharmacy. The PBOP provides for this purpose that "immediate building" means the physical structure that contains the pharmacy, and where a pharmacy is located in a complex consisting of multiple retail and other business establishments, such as a mall, the pharmacy is not considered to be located within these retail establishments. In these situations, the entire store containing the pharmacy is licensed and the pharmacist shall remain in the store during a break.

b. While on break, the pharmacist must be accessible for emergencies or for patient counseling.

c. The pharmacy may remain open during the pharmacist's break for patient-related services by the pharmacy technicians and/or pharmacy interns that remain in the pharmacy. The services that may occur include receiving new written prescriptions, preparing prescriptions for final verification by the pharmacist, and delivery of prescription medications that have already been verified by the pharmacist. However, if there is an emergency or if a patient requests or accepts counseling, the pharmacist must return to the pharmacy.

STUDY TIP: Remember, a pharmacist may take up to a 30-minute meal break but cannot leave the premises. The pharmacy is not considered closed during this time, and pharmacy technicians and interns may remain in the pharmacy.

---

14. Permit renewal requirements for pharmacies:
   a. Pharmacy permits must be renewed by application every 2 years before September 1 of each odd numbered year.
   b. The PBOP will not renew a pharmacy permit if the applicant or its partners or officers were determined to have violated any federal or state law relating to the practice of pharmacy or controlled substances.
   c. If the pharmacy permit holder does not renew on time, it must stop operations until the license or permit is renewed. Operating a pharmacy with an expired permit could result in disciplinary actions and additional fees.
   d. A pharmacy permit holder that has been authorized by another state to ship, mail, or deliver prescription medications to patients in that state must report this information on the Pennsylvania biennial registration application.

15. A pharmacy may not display, advertise, or use any name other than the name it is registered under.

16. A pharmacy shall maintain a supply of drugs and devices adequate to meet the needs of the health professions and the patients it is intended to serve. The permit application

requires the pharmacy to show by affidavit that it has ordered and will maintain an inventory of nonproprietary drugs, devices, and equipment appropriate to the practice of that pharmacy. The inventory must include at least $5,000 worth of nonproprietary drugs and devices, at cost, from a licensed wholesaler or manufacturer. The inventory may not go below this figure at any time. A central processing center is not required to maintain $5,000 worth of nonproprietary drugs and devices.

Note: Pharmacy inventories far exceed $5,000; however, this specific amount is still listed in the Board rule.

17. Drugs that have expired, been improperly stored, or are adulterated or misbranded must be removed from the active stock and properly disposed of by the pharmacist manager (or one delegated by the pharmacist manager). Controlled substances must be disposed of by DEA standards, and a record of disposal must show the date and manner of disposal and the number of units that were disposed.

18. Pharmacies (except for central processing centers) must maintain the following minimum equipment and supplies:
    a. A refrigerator kept in the prescription area used solely for storage of drugs and equipped with a temperature monitoring device.
    b. Prescription files for keeping prescriptions, where the original prescription or image of the original shall be retained for 2 years from the date of most recent filling. A pharmacy can use a computerized recordkeeping system for keeping track of refills.
    c. Current copies of the Pennsylvania Pharmacy Act and Pennsylvania State Board of Pharmacy Rules, and any other federal and state laws and rules that pertain to pharmacy practice.
    d. Necessary equipment and supplies that allow the pharmacy to properly prepare and dispense prescriptions within the scope of practice.
    e. An adequate reference library that enables a pharmacy to properly prepare and dispense prescriptions at that location and that:
       (1) includes current reference sources appropriate for that practice type;

    (2) allows for the safe and effective compounding of medications;

    (3) lists the possible drug interactions and adverse effects of medications;

    (4) lists the therapeutic equivalents for medications;

    (5) lists the usage and dosages of medications dispensed; and

    (6) provides guidelines for the counseling of patients.
    Note: A pharmacy that specializes in nuclear or parenteral prescriptions may limit the library it maintains to the pharmacy's own specialization.

  f. A pharmacy operating as a central processing center must maintain equipment, supplies, and access to a reference library recognized by the pharmacy community as meeting minimum standards of practice as a central processing center.

19. The pharmacy displays its permit in a conspicuous place in the pharmacy. The pharmacy may not post or display in public view a current certificate, license, permit, registration, or renewal of a person not lawfully employed by the pharmacy.

20. Any disciplinary action taken by other states must be reported to the PBOP within 30 days of final disposition.

B. Construction and Security Requirements for Pharmacy Permits (PBOP Rule 49 Pa. Code §§ 27.16–27.17)

  1. Approval of Pharmacy Plans

    a. New pharmacy or change-of-location—plans for construction of a new pharmacy or new location for an existing pharmacy may be submitted to the PBOP for approval prior to proceeding with construction. Within 90 days of submission, the PBOP will notify the applicant of its approval or disapproval and reasons. The plans, including dimensions, must demonstrate compliance with applicable regulations and show the layout and fixtures for the prescription area and the immediately adjacent area.

    b. Alterations—while substantial alterations are being made to a pharmacy, the practice of pharmacy shall stop unless the pharmacy submits the alterations and a safety plan to the PBOP 30 days prior and the PBOP does not object.

2. Building Standards
    a. The minimum size of the prescription area must be at least 250 square feet and must be large enough to carry on the practice of pharmacy in a manner that protects the health and safety of professionals, employees, and the public. The prescription area must have a prescription working counter of at least 10 linear feet in length and 2 linear feet in width. When two pharmacists are on duty at the same time, the minimum counter length must be increased by 5 linear feet for an additional pharmacist. Institutions with special considerations may apply to the Board for a waiver of these requirements. A pharmacy operating as a central processing center is not required to meet the minimum space requirements.
    b. Retail pharmacies located in retail establishments with business hours that differ must meet the following requirements:
        (1) The pharmacy must be able to be securely sealed off from the remainder of the retail establishment.
        (2) The barrier device that seals off the pharmacy must reach from the floor to the ceiling, must provide security from access to anything in the pharmacy, and must be securely locked when a pharmacist is not on duty.
        (3) The pharmacy shall be closed whenever a pharmacist is not present in the immediate building and on duty.
        (4) Safes, equipment, or other facilities of the establishment cannot be located in a manner that one needs to go through the pharmacy, unless a pharmacist is on duty whenever staff needs access.
        (5) Hours of the pharmacy must be posted at all points of public access.
        (6) Protocols must be in place, including notification of the pharmacy manager for when the pharmacy is closed and a non-pharmacist staff needs access for emergencies (e.g., fires, police matters).
    c. The prescription area of a pharmacy must have a substantially constructed cabinet or safe for controlled substances unless the pharmacy disperses throughout the

stock of non-controlled substances. If a pharmacy carries Schedule I controlled substances, these must be stored in a securely locked cabinet or safe.

    d. A pharmacy must have at least one telephone accessible in the prescription area, and the pharmacy telephone number must be printed on the prescription label.

    e. Except for central processing centers, pharmacies must have a sink in the prescription area that has hot and cold water and that can only be used for pharmaceutical purposes. Restroom facilities for pharmacy employees shall be close to the pharmacy, but outside of the prescription area.

    f. The pharmacy must be well lighted and ventilated.

    g. There can be no televisions within the prescription area or situated in a manner that can be seen from the prescription area.

    h. The prescription area must be arranged so that medications cannot be accessed by an unlicensed or unauthorized person, and the area cannot be used for storage of items other than those needed for the preparation, dispensing, and delivery of drugs.

    3. Security of Schedule II controlled substances is the same as federal law. Pharmacies in Pennsylvania can store CII medications in securely locked, substantially constructed cabinets, or dispersed throughout non-controlled stock in a manner to obstruct theft (*see PBOP Rule 49 Pa. Code § 27.17*). The pharmacy manager is responsible for ensuring those that enter the prescription area know and abide by the standards of security.

C. Requirements for Institutional Pharmacies (PBOP Rules 49 Pa. Code §§ 27.41 and 27.42)

    1. Institutional pharmacies do not require a different or special type of permit from the PBOP; however, there are additional requirements that must be met to obtain and maintain a pharmacy permit.

    2. To be considered by the PBOP for a pharmacy permit, an institution must be accredited, licensed, and/or meet additional conditions. The PBOP requirements include accreditation by the Joint Commission on Accreditation of Hospitals or the Commission on Hospital Accreditation of the American Osteopathic Association, meeting federal conditions of participation for extended care facilities or the Federal Health Insurance for the Aged, and/or being licensed by the Pennsylvania Department of Welfare or Department of Health.

3. An institution may not be considered for a pharmacy permit unless the pharmacy in that institution is open a minimum of 20 hours per week under the supervision of a registered pharmacist manager.

4. Pharmaceutical services provided in institutions must always meet the Pennsylvania Department of Health and Department of Welfare rules and regulations, which are incorporated automatically into the PBOP regulations. Violations of the Department of Health or Department of Welfare rules constitute a violation under the PBOP rules. For additional details on the Pennsylvania Department of Health Rules. *See Chapter 4, Section V*

D. Other Required Registrations or Approvals

1. Cancer Drug Repository Program Approval (PBOP Rules 49 Pa. Code §§ 27.501–27.506)

   a. A Pennsylvania pharmacy with a current unrestricted permit may apply for approval to participate in the state's Cancer Drug Repository Program, which allows unused cancer drugs to be re-dispensed to cancer patients. The application must include a certification from a licensed pharmacist employed by the pharmacy that the pharmacist and pharmacy will comply with program requirements.

   b. Once approved for the program, the pharmacist at the pharmacy can accept eligible donated cancer drugs from a pharmacy, healthcare facility, drug manufacturer, or wholesale drug distributor. The donated drugs must be accompanied by a repository donor form.

   c. Eligible drugs include those in the original unopened, sealed, and tamper-evident unit dose packaging, including single unit doses in unopened packaging even when the outside packaging is opened.

   d. Ineligible drugs include those with an expiration date earlier than 6 months from the date the drug will be restocked by the participating pharmacy; drugs that appear to be adulterated or misbranded; compounded drugs; drugs that are controlled substances; or drugs that require refrigeration or other special temperature requirements beyond controlled room temperature.

e. The pharmacy accepting the drugs must have a designated area separate from the regular pharmacy area for receiving and storing the drugs.

f. Drugs that are not eligible or that have been recalled must be destroyed or disposed of properly and a record kept in the pharmacy for at least 2 years.

g. After receiving a prescription for an eligible patient, and prior to dispensing a cancer drug under the program, the pharmacy must inform the patient that it was previously dispensed but was unused and donated, and the patient must sign a cancer drug repository informed consent form, which must be maintained at the pharmacy for 2 years.

h. Donated drugs must be accounted for by the pharmacy through proper recordkeeping. Detailed records must be kept for 2 years for drugs received, dispensed, distributed, or disposed of.

i. A pharmacy may charge a state-set handling fee for dispensing a covered product.

j. A prescription for a covered product can only be dispensed to an eligible patient. Eligibility requirements include a lack of drug coverage for the prescribed medications, the patient is not eligible for state Medicaid, and the patient meets state-determined income limits.

2. Nonresident Pharmacy Registration (63 P. S. § 390-4.1)

a. Required for pharmacies located outside of Pennsylvania that ship, mail, or deliver, in any manner, a dispensed medicinal drug into Pennsylvania.

b. A nonresident pharmacy must apply to the PBOP and obtain a certificate of registration to conduct a pharmacy in Pennsylvania. The application requires information about the nonresident pharmacy and the name of the pharmacist in charge. A nonresident pharmacy must then continue to register on a biennial basis with the PBOP to maintain its certificate of registration to conduct a pharmacy.

c. A nonresident pharmacy must report to the Board within 30 days after any change of location or pharmacist in charge.

d. The nonresident pharmacy application requires a statement that the pharmacy complies with all the laws in the state it is located in and that it will comply with requests for information made by the PBOP. A copy of the most recent inspection report from the state agency where the pharmacy is located must also be submitted.

e. The nonresident pharmacy must maintain a valid unexpired pharmacy permit in compliance with the laws of the state in which the nonresident pharmacy is located.

f. A nonresident pharmacy must report to the PBOP within 30 days the final disposition of any disciplinary action taken by the regulatory or licensing agency of the state in which the nonresident pharmacy is located.

g. A nonresident pharmacy must be open at least 6 days per week and for a minimum of 40 hours per week. The nonresident pharmacy must provide a toll-free telephone number (on its pharmacy label) for Pennsylvania patients to communicate with the pharmacist at the nonresident pharmacy if desired.

h. The PBOP may deny, revoke, or suspend any certificate of registration of a nonresident pharmacy for conduct which causes injury to a Pennsylvania resident, or for any discipline received by another agency outside of Pennsylvania.

i. It is unlawful for a nonresident pharmacy that has not been issued a certificate of registration by the PBOP to advertise its services in Pennsylvania.

VII. The Pennsylvania Drugs, Devices and Cosmetics Program
A. Introduction
1. The Pennsylvania Drugs, Devices and Cosmetics Program applies to businesses in Pennsylvania that manufacture, distribute, or retail drugs. Depending on the activity, the program requires registration with the Department of Health and licensure with the state. There are exemptions to registration and licensure, which often apply to pharmacies.
2. The majority of the laws and rules under the Pennsylvania Drug Device and Cosmetic Program apply to manufacturers and distributors, but there are relevant sections that apply to pharmacies and pharmacists.

3. The list of state statutes and regulations that pertain to the Pennsylvania Drug Device and Cosmetic program can be found on the Pennsylvania Department of Health website at *https://www.health.pa.gov/topics/programs/Pages/Drugs-Devices-and-Cosmetics.aspx.* This list primarily includes the Pennsylvania Drug Device and Cosmetic Act and Regulations, the Pennsylvania Generic Equivalent Drug Law and Regulations, the Pennsylvania Noncontrolled Substances Reporting and Registration Act, and the Pennsylvania Wholesale Prescription Drug Distributors License Act.

4. The Pennsylvania Controlled Substance, Drug Device and Cosmetic Act (PCSDDCA) and Rules (PCSDDCR) have similarities to the Federal Food, Drug, and Cosmetic Act (FDCA) discussed in Chapter 1 and the Federal Controlled Substances Act (FCSA) discussed in Chapter 2. The sections of the PCSDDCA and PCSDDCR that apply to pharmacy practice and controlled substances were already discussed in Chapter 2. The Pennsylvania Generic Equivalent Drug Law and Regulations will be discussed in detail in Chapter 4, as these primarily apply to pharmacies and pharmacists. The following information provided in the below sections of this chapter will focus on a number of the other legal or regulatory requirements under the Pennsylvania Drug Device and Cosmetic Program that are not covered elsewhere in this text and that impact pharmacy practice or may be included in the MPJE competency statements.

B. General Considerations of the Pennsylvania Drug Device and Cosmetic Program

1. Each business location in Pennsylvania that manufactures, compounds under 503B, distributes, or retails drugs (prescription, controlled substances, or OTC), medical devices, and/or medicated cosmetics must register with the Pennsylvania Department of Health under the Pennsylvania Drug Device and Cosmetic Program and obtain a Certificate of Registration. In addition, any distributor of prescription drugs or controlled substances needs to obtain a Certificate of Licensure and comply with the licensure requirements under the Pennsylvania Wholesale Prescription Drug Distributors Licensure Act (Act 145 of 1992). Therefore, any wholesale distributor of prescription drugs or controlled

substances located in Pennsylvania that handles product needs both registration and licensure.

2. In general, Pennsylvania licensed pharmacies solely engaged in the practice of pharmacy are regulated by the PBOP and do not need to register with the Department of Health or obtain licensure as a wholesale distributor. However, if a pharmacy or its employees engage in activities beyond the scope of pharmacy practice, it may need to register or obtain licensure. Examples may include:

   a. Wholesale distribution;

   b. Manufacturing or compounding drugs that are not for specific patients or prescription orders;

   c. Operating as a separate retailer of over-the-counter drug products when no pharmacist is on duty; and

   d. Engaging in other activities that are beyond the scope of practice of pharmacy.

3. A pharmacy may distribute minimal quantities of no more than 5% of their annual total prescription drug sales to licensed practitioners for use within their practice (e.g., for office use) without having to become licensed as a distributer.

   Note: Pennsylvania clearly points out that obtaining a distribution license/registration does not authorize a licensed pharmacy to act as a wholesale distributor, exceed 5% distribution, or distribute to other pharmacies or distributors. It further explains that both federal and state laws clearly outlined a limited exemption for a licensed pharmacy to distribute because the federal and state laws never intended for a pharmacy to act as a distributor. Thus, a wholesale distributor license and registration are separate from any pharmacy license, and all inventory, product, storage, records, etc. are separate from the pharmacy. Therefore, a pharmacy should stay under the 5% rule, and if it plans to obtain a wholesale distribution license, it should only do so for its intended purposes, meaning actively and physically receiving, storing, and distributing product under the license, as well as be prepared to comply with the additional federal and state laws that apply to distributors.

4. Medical oxygen used for human consumption is generally considered a prescription drug under federal and

Pennsylvania law. Facilities that manufacture oxygen must register with the Department of Health, while facilities that purchase and resell oxygen to another facility or supply it directly to the ultimate user must register as a distributor of prescription products. However, pharmacies and healthcare facilities are exempt from registration if dispensing oxygen to their own patients.

5. State licensed pharmacies may prepackage (repackage) medications to use after the receipt of a valid prescription for an identified, individual patient. While this type of activity requires pharmacies to meet certain standards, such as assigning the repackaged product a beyond-use date, it does not require the pharmacy to register as a manufacturer, repackager, and/or distributor. However, if the activity goes beyond that permitted by a licensed pharmacy, such as distributing the repackaged product to other facilities for use other than for use after the receipt of patient specific prescriptions, the pharmacy may be required under federal and state law to register the repackaging facility. To avoid this concern, pharmacies should review state and federal laws and not exceed the scope of what is permitted. In addition to having to consider FDA registration, in Pennsylvania a repackaging facility would need to meet the requirements under the Pennsylvania Wholesale Prescription Drug Distributors License Act.

STUDY TIP: There is no specific Pennsylvania rule that addresses beyond-use dating (BUD) for prepackaging of unit-dose packaging of solid oral dosage units. The FDA and USP have provided guidance that includes following the manufacturer's labeling or, if that is not available, to refer to USP standards or the manufacturer's expiration date, whichever is sooner. The long-standing USP standard providing for a 1-year BUD or the manufacturer's expiration date, whichever is sooner, for repackaged unit-dose medications in hospitals is still commonly followed.

CHAPTER FOUR

Pennsylvania Laws—Part 2
Pharmacy Personnel, Pharmacy
Practice, and Disciplinary Matters

I. **Laws and Rules Applicable to Individuals**

   A. Pharmacists (PBOP Rules 49 Pa. Code §§ 27.12 and 27.19)
Practice of Pharmacy and Delegation of Duties
It is unlawful for a person not licensed as a pharmacist by the PBOP to engage in or allow another person to engage in the practice of pharmacy. While there are certain aspects of the practice of pharmacy that a pharmacist can delegate to a pharmacy intern or pharmacy technician, there are specific functions that can only be performed by a pharmacist. Functions that must be performed by a pharmacist include:

     1. Review every prescription or drug order prior to it being dispensed to determine the name of the drug, strength, dosage, quantity, permissible refills, and other required information and to verify the accuracy of the preparation.

     2. Provide direct, immediate, and personal supervision to interns and technicians working with the pharmacist (this includes reviewing and verifying the prescription and final product and being immediately available upon the premises to direct the work of the interns and technicians and respond to questions and problems).

     3. Ensure that the pharmacy label on the prescription medication being dispensed meets all label requirements.

     4. Counseling of patients.
Note: PBOP Rule 49 Pa. Code § 27.19 states that "only a pharmacist can counsel"; therefore, pharmacy interns in Pennsylvania are not permitted to counsel patients, even under the direct supervision of a pharmacist.

   B. Pharmacy Technicians (PBOP Rule 49 Pa. Code § 27.12)

     1. Delegable Tasks
This rule sets forth those tasks that a pharmacist may delegate to a pharmacy technician. These include:

       a. Carry containers of drugs in and around the pharmacy.

       b. Count pills, tablets, and capsules and put them in containers.

   c. Type and/or print labels.

   d. Maintain records which are related to the practice of pharmacy.

   e. Assist the pharmacist in preparing and reconstituting parenteral products and other medications.
Note: This PBOP rule also states that the pharmacist is to initial the label of the final product to document final inspection and accept total responsibility for its preparation.

   f. Enter prescription, drug order, or patient information in a patient profile.

   g. Assist the pharmacist in the compounding of drug products.

STUDY TIP: Usually, pharmacists can only delegate to a pharmacy technician non-discretionary tasks, or tasks that do not involve independent professional judgment. This is the only current mention of pharmacy technicians in the PBOP rules at this time; although the PPA has been amended to regulate pharmacy technicians further, it will take time for additional rules to be passed regarding pharmacy technicians.

---

  2. Non-Delegable Tasks and Written Protocol Requirements
This rule sets forth those tasks and functions that a pharmacist may NOT delegate to a pharmacy technician and that a technician may not perform, as well as providing for the requirement of written protocols for pharmacy technicians. These include:

   a. Accept or transcribe an oral order or telephone prescription.

   b. Enter or be in a pharmacy if a pharmacist is not on duty.

   c. Perform any act within the practice of pharmacy that involves discretion or independent professional judgment.

   d. Perform a duty until the technician has been trained and the duty has been specified in a written protocol.

     (1) The pharmacist manager is required to create and maintain a written protocol for each pharmacy technician employed in the pharmacy.

     (2) The written protocol must specify each duty which the pharmacy technician may perform.

(3) The pharmacist manager and the pharmacy technician must date and sign the protocol and each amendment to it.

(4) When requested by an agent of the Board, the pharmacist manager must make the protocol available.

   3. Pharmacy Technician Data Entry (63 P. S. § 390-3.4)

      a. The PPA was amended in 2020 allowing a pharmacy technician to conduct data entry, including prescription entry, drug order, or patient information, into a patient profile via technological means without the immediate supervision of a board-licensed pharmacist if all of the following apply:

(1) The pharmacy has documented policies and procedures and other adequate safeguards to protect against patient harm and privacy incidents.

(2) The pharmacy technician is adequately trained to perform the data entry task.

(3) A supervising pharmacist is readily available to answer questions of the pharmacy technician and is responsible for the practice and accuracy of the pharmacy technician.

(4) No part of the data entry includes any direct interaction with prescription medication.

      b. This amendment to the PPA will allow data entry by a pharmacy technician at a remote location, without a supervising pharmacist on the premises with the technician. As with the other PPA amendments regarding pharmacy technicians, PBOP rules will need to be promulgated to implement the law.

   4. Pennsylvania does not currently have any rules, requirements, or limitations regarding pharmacy technician ratios.

STUDY TIP: Non-pharmacist personnel ratios is a topic included in the MPJE competency statements. Since Pennsylvania does not have any rules regarding ratios for non-pharmacist personnel, one would not expect to see a question on this.

  C. Pharmacy Interns (PBOP Rule 49 Pa. Code § 27.12)

   1. A pharmacy intern may work only under the direct, immediate, personal supervision of a pharmacist. A pharmacy intern may perform procedures which require professional skill and training. Examples of these procedures include verifying ingredients, weighing ingredients, compounding ingredients, and other similar processing of ingredients. *Note: This implies that a registered pharmacy intern can perform the same acts as a pharmacist when under the direct and immediate supervision of a Pennsylvania licensed pharmacist (except those acts that are expressly reserved for a pharmacist, such as the final verification of a prescription and patient counseling). This means that an intern can perform those duties that a pharmacy technician cannot perform, such as receiving verbal prescriptions.*

2. A pharmacy intern is only permitted to enter or be in a pharmacy when a pharmacist is on duty.

STUDY TIP: Recall that a registered pharmacy intern can become authorized to immunize under the direct, immediate supervision of an authorized pharmacist. However, to participate in this activity, the intern must obtain a separate authorization from the PBOP.

II. **Laws, Rules, and Practice Standards for Pharmacy Permits or Pharmacists**
   Note: In general, the practice standards listed apply to all practice settings (i.e., community and institutional); however, some standards were specifically written for certain practice settings. For those that don't distinguish between practice settings, it is likely that some of these practices only take place in certain settings, and various rules seem to be clearly written just for community pharmacies.

   A. Time Limits on Filling or Refilling Prescriptions (PBOP Rule 49 Pa. Code § 27.18)
      1. Prescriptions for non-controlled drugs can be refilled for 1 year from the date of the prescription if refills were authorized by the prescriber. This also applies to prescriptions that contain PRN refills.
         Note: Since refills expire after 1 year, if a prescription that was issued or written was never filled, it would also expire 1 year from the date of the prescription.
      2. For controlled substance prescriptions (*see Chapter 2*), Schedule II controlled substances may not be filled more than 6 months from the date of the prescription, and there

can be no refills on Schedule II prescriptions. A controlled substance in Schedule III, IV, or V may not be filled or refilled more than 5 times in the 6-month period from the date of the prescription.

3. A pharmacist may only refill a prescription at a reasonable time prior to the time when the contents of the prescription shall be consumed according to prescriber's directions.
    Note: The pharmacist should use professional judgment when addressing requests for early fills or refills. In determining what a reasonable time is, companies or insurance plans may provide specific requirements regarding how many days early a prescription can be filled or refilled. The PA PDMP also defines an early refill as when the patient requests a refill prior to the date when they are eligible for insurance coverage for the prescription, or when more than 15% of an earlier-dispensed medication would remain when taken in compliance with the directions and quantity prescribed.

4. A pharmacist cannot fill or refill a prescription for a patient which was written for prior use by a prescriber who is deceased or no longer in practice. *See Chapter 3, Section II. B.3.*

5. Emergency Prescription Refills (63 P. S. § 390-8(2.1))
    a. In the event a pharmacist receives a request for a prescription refill and the pharmacist is unable to readily obtain refill authorization from the prescriber, the pharmacist may dispense:
        (1) a onetime emergency refill of up to a 72-hour supply of the prescribed medication; or
        (2) a onetime emergency refill of an amount not to exceed a 30-day supply of the prescribed drug, but only if the medication is not dispensed or sold in a 72-hour supply.
        Note: Medications that are available as tablets and capsules can easily be dispensed as a 72-hour supply. The 30-day supply allowance was intended to cover medications such as insulin, where the packaging cannot be broken to meet the 72-hour limitation.
    b. Other requirements:
        (1) The medication involved is not a controlled substance.

- **(2)** The medication involved is essential to the maintenance of life and the continuation of therapy in chronic conditions.
- **(3)** In the pharmacist's professional judgment, the interruption of therapy might produce an undesirable health consequence, be detrimental to the patient's welfare, or cause physical or mental discomfort for the patient.
- **(4)** The pharmacist enters on the back of the original prescription or other retrievable record the date and quantity of the refill and signs the refill.
- **(5)** Within 72 hours of dispensing the medication the pharmacist notifies the prescriber that the emergency refill was dispensed.

STUDY TIP: Pennsylvania does not allow emergency refills for controlled substances. A new prescription would need to be obtained to provide a controlled substance medication to a patient that is out of refills.

- **B.** Pharmacy Labels (PBOP Rule 49 Pa. Code § 27.18; PCSDDCA § 11(f); PCSDDCR 28 Pa. Code § 25.94; Pennsylvania Generic Equivalent Drug Law (35 P. S. § 960.3(e)))
  - **1.** Community or outpatient pharmacy labels—The pharmacy label placed on the container of a prescription medication that is dispensed to a patient is required to contain specific information. The following list incorporates requirements from various federal and state laws and rules, including PBOP and Department of Health Rules:
    - **a.** The name, address, telephone number, and DEA number of the pharmacy;
    - **b.** The name of the patient;
    - **c.** Full directions for the use of its contents;
    - **d.** The name of the prescriber;
    - **e.** The serial number of the prescription;
    - **f.** The date the prescription was originally filled and the date of filling;
    - **g.** The trade or brand name of the drug, strength, dosage form, and quantity dispensed; and if a generic drug is dispensed, the generic name and the manufacturer's/distributor's name or abbreviation must also be shown;

h. The manufacturer's expiration date of the medication must be included on the pharmacy label when, at the time of dispensing, the medication has full potency for less than one year (as determined by the expiration date placed on the original label by the manufacturer); and *Note: The pharmacy label should include the statement "Do not use after [manufacturer's expiration date]" or similar wording when the manufacturer's expiration date is less than 1 year.*

i. On controlled substances, the statement "Caution: Federal law prohibits the transfer of this drug to any person other than the patient for whom it was prescribed."

STUDY TIP: The "Caution" warning statement is required for all dispensed CII–CV medications in Pennsylvania, while federal law only requires the warning for dispensed CII–CIV medications. Since Pennsylvania law is stricter than federal law, it would need to be followed. Many pharmacies place the statement on all controlled and non-controlled prescriptions dispensed; however, it is only required on CII–CV medications.

---

2. A drug (or medication) order in an institution is not required to conform to the same labeling requirements just listed as long as it is dispensed in unit dose. A drug not in unit dose packaging must be labeled with the following:
   a. Patient name;
   b. Drug name;
   c. Drug strength;
   d. Dosing instructions; and
   e. Lot number.

3. If the drug order in an institution is a parenteral, enteral, or total nutritional product, it must be labeled with the following:
   a. Patient name;
   b. Product ingredients including:
      (1) name of each ingredient
      (2) strength of each ingredient
      (3) quantity of each ingredient
      (4) diluent
      (5) expiration date; and
   c. Initials of the pharmacist.

4. Labeling of Prepackaged Products
   a. The container of a prepackaged product shall have a label that includes:
      (1) The name of the drug, and if the drug is generic the name of the manufacturer;
      (2) The strength of the drug; and
      (3) The expiration date.
   b. The pharmacy must also keep a log stating all the above listed information as well as the date and quantity of medication that was prepacked.

C. Prescription Records and Files (PBOP Rule 49 Pa. Code § 27.18)
   1. Prescription files kept at the pharmacy must show:
      a. Name and address of the patient;
      b. Name and address of the prescriber;
      c. The date the prescription was issued (if the prescription is for a controlled substance or if it was written with a PRN or ad lib refill designation);
         Note: The PBOP (see PBOP Rule 49 Pa. Code § 27.18(b)(1)) only requires an issuance date for prescriptions that are for controlled substances or issued for PRN refills; however, oftentimes the issuance date may still be required for other reasons, such as insurance and payment purposes. In addition, the PBOP (see PBOP Rule 49 Pa. Code § 27.18(i)) also provides that prescription medications may only be refilled for 1 year from the date of the prescription if refills have been authorized. The pharmacist would need to know the date of issuance to determine the expiration of prescription refills.
      d. The name and quantity of the drug prescribed;
      e. Directions for use;
      f. Cautions communicated to the patient when dispensed;
      g. The date the prescription was compounded and dispensed; and
      h. The name or initials of the dispensing pharmacist.
         Note: When a prescriber issues a prescription, it is required to have the patient's name on it. If the patient's name is missing, the pharmacist would need to properly address this concern prior to dispensing the prescription in order to meet the pharmacy labeling and recordkeeping requirements. However, the PBOP has provided for a specific situation that would allow a missing patient's name

to be addressed after dispensing the prescription. When a pharmacist receives a prescription for a radiopharmaceutical for a patient whose name is unavailable at the time the prescription is received and the pharmacist dispenses the product, the pharmacist is permitted to do this if the patient's name is obtained within 72 hours after dispensing the radiopharmaceutical. See PBOP Statement of Policy 49 Pa. Code § 27.101

2. Prescriptions on file for controlled substances must also show the DEA number of the prescriber and meet all other DEA and state requirements.

   Note: See Chapter 2 for information regarding DEA and Pennsylvania requirements. An example of a DEA and Pennsylvania requirement would be that the prescriber must manually sign a written prescription unless it is electronically prescribed.

3. For prescriptions that have refills, each refill must have a record showing the following:

   a. Date of the refill;

   b. Name or initials of the dispensing pharmacist; and

   c. Quantity dispensed (if the pharmacist dispenses a quantity different from the original prescription, the pharmacist must indicate the changes on the back of the original prescription or enter the changes in the computerized files of the pharmacy).

4. Original prescriptions or readily retrievable images of the original prescriptions shall be kept for 2 years from the date of the most recent filling.

5. In an institution, Schedule II controlled substances which the pharmacy dispensed and were received by the patient shall be recorded and the record kept for 2 years.

D. Prescription Transfers and Common Database (63 P. S. § 390-4(a)(3.1))

1. Transfers of prescriptions between pharmacies in Pennsylvania is permissible under the following conditions:

   a. The prescription is for a drug which is lawfully refillable;

   b. The drug is not a Schedule II controlled substance; and

   c. The pharmacist transferring the prescription cancels the original prescription in his/her records and indicates on the prescription records to whom the prescription was transferred, including the name of the pharmacy, the date of transfer, and the name or initials of the transferring pharmacist.

    d. The pharmacist receiving the transferred prescription:

        (1) Notes on the prescription that it is a transferred prescription; and

        (2) Records the following:

            (i) Date of issuance of original prescription;

            (ii) Date of original filing of prescription;

            (iii) Original number of refills authorized on prescription;

            (iv) Complete refill record from original prescription; and

            (v) Number of valid refills remaining.

STUDY TIP: Recall that DEA only allows the transfer of refills and not of original prescriptions for controlled substances, although by policy, they allow original prescriptions to be transferred if they are electronic prescriptions for controlled substances. *See Chapter 2, Section VIII. B.*

---

  2. Common Database

    a. A pharmacist may transfer a prescription to another pharmacist employed by the same corporation without meeting 1.c. and 1.d. above if both pharmacists have access to the same computerized prescription transfer system.

    b. The computerized prescription system must contain the prescription and refill records and incorporate procedures to prevent unauthorized refills.

STUDY TIP: Be sure you understand the difference between a transfer and dispensing from a common database.

E. OBRA '90—Patient Profiles, PDRs, and Counseling

  1. Requirement for Patient Profiles (PBOP Rule 49 Pa. Code § 27.19(f))

    a. The pharmacist or designee of the pharmacist (e.g., pharmacy technician or intern) must begin a patient profile when the pharmacist fills a prescription for a new patient.

    b. The pharmacist or designee of the pharmacist must make a reasonable effort to obtain, record, and maintain the following information about each patient:

(1) Name of the patient;

(2) Address and telephone number of the patient;

(3) Age or date of birth of the patient;

(4) Patient's gender;

(5) The patient's individual history, if significant, including known allergies and drug reactions, and a list of medications and relevant devices as provided by the patient or caregiver; and

(6) Pharmacist's comments relevant to patient's drug therapy.

Note: *The PBOP considers a single request for information for a patient profile made to a patient or caregiver a reasonable effort.*

c. A pharmacist is not required to obtain information for the patient profile if the patient or caregiver refuses to provide information. A failure to respond to a request for information is also deemed a refusal.

d. The pharmacist or designee must document when a patient or caregiver refuses to provide information for a patient profile. The documentation must include the name or initials of the pharmacist or designee noting the refusal. Examples of documentation include a notation on the prescription, patient profile, or electronic record of the pharmacy, or a writing signed by the patient or caregiver.

e. Patient profiles may be maintained electronically or manually and must be maintained for at least 2 years after the last entry.

2. Prospective Drug Review (PDR) (PBOP Rule 49 Pa. Code § 27.19(a–c), (e))

a. The purpose of the PDR is to help ensure that a prescription drug being dispensed is not likely to have an adverse medical result. A pharmacist must perform a PDR before filling, delivering, or sending a new prescription or drug order. The PDR requires that the pharmacist review the patient profile maintained in the pharmacy prior to dispensing a medication. The pharmacist is to attempt to identify potential drug therapy problems that might result from the following:

(1) Therapeutic duplication;

(2) Drug-drug interactions;

(3) Incorrect drug dosage or duration of treatment;

(4) Drug-allergy interactions; and

(5) Clinical abuse/misuse.

b. Upon recognizing any of the above, the pharmacist must intervene to attempt to resolve the problem. This could include, for example, consultation with the prescriber.

c. The PBOP has provided additional information regarding the scope of a PDR, including examples of when a PDR is and is not required to be performed. Examples of situations of when a PDR is required for prescriptions and drug orders include:

(1) A patient visits a physician in the physician's office and receives a prescription. The patient has the prescription filled in a retail pharmacy.

(2) A pharmacist fills a prescription for a patient who lives in a personal care home.

(3) A pharmacist in a hospital pharmacy fills an outpatient prescription for a hospital employee.

(4) A patient is treated on a non-emergency basis in an outpatient clinic of a hospital and is given a prescription. The patient has the prescription filled either in the hospital pharmacy or in a retail pharmacy.

(5) A pharmacist fills a prescription for a patient in a nursing home.

(6) A pharmacist in a hospital dispenses a drug which will be administered to a patient in the hospital.

d. Examples of situations when a PDR is not required include:

(1) A physician dispenses a drug to a patient being treated in the emergency room.

(2) A pharmacist dispenses a radiopharmaceutical to a physician who will administer it to a patient.

(3) A medical practitioner dispenses a drug.

(4) A pharmacist dispenses a drug to a medical practitioner which the practitioner will administer to a patient.

(5) A pharmacist delivers naloxone to an identified employee of a Pennsylvania correctional facility, prison, jail, or residential drug treatment facility under a prescription and for an identified individual who is pending release or discharge from the correctional facility, prison, jail, or residential drug treatment facility.

3. Patient Counseling (PBOP Rule 49 Pa. Code § 27.19(e), (g))

    a. An offer to counsel shall be made to each patient or caregiver when the pharmacist fills, delivers, or sends a new retail or outpatient prescription.

    b. The pharmacist or designee of the pharmacist shall orally make the offer in person if a patient or caregiver comes to the pharmacy. If the pharmacist, in the exercise of professional judgment and in the interest of a patient, believes that an oral offer would be less effective than a written offer, the pharmacist may substitute a written offer. Examples may include when the patient or caregiver is hearing impaired or does not speak English.

STUDY TIP: Pennsylvania does not have mandatory patient counseling, but does require an offer to counsel for new prescriptions.

---

    c. If neither the patient nor caregiver comes to the pharmacy, the offer to counsel must be made by meeting one of the following methods listed:

        (1) The pharmacist or designee telephoning the patient or caregiver;

        (2) The pharmacy delivery person orally making the offer to the patient or caregiver; or

        (3) The pharmacist sending a written offer to counsel together with the filled prescription, which is delivered or sent to the patient. If a written offer to counsel is used, it must include the telephone number of the pharmacy, and it must be a toll-free telephone service if its primary patient population is beyond the local or toll-free exchange.

        Note: A mail-order pharmacy is only permitted to make the offer to counsel either by telephone or by sending a written offer together with the filled prescription. The written offer must include a toll-free telephone number of the pharmacy that a patient or caregiver may use to obtain counseling.

    d. If the patient or caregiver does not refuse the offer to counsel, or if one indicates that he/she wants counseling, only a pharmacist may provide the counseling. When the patient or caregiver is at the pharmacy, the counseling shall occur in person or at the discretion of the patient or caregiver by telephone. When a prescription is delivered to the patient or caregiver, the counseling is to be performed by telephone.

Note: In Pennsylvania, only a pharmacist is allowed to counsel a patient or caregiver. Pharmacy interns are not permitted to counsel, even under the direct supervision of a pharmacist.

e. The following are examples of matters which a pharmacist in the exercise of professional judgment might deem significant and discuss with the patient or caregiver while counseling:

(1) Name and description of the drug;

(2) Dosage form, dose, route of administration, and duration of therapy;

(3) Intended use of the drug and expected action;

(4) Special directions and precautions for preparation, administration, and use;

(5) Common severe side effects or interactions and therapeutic contraindications that may be encountered, including their avoidance, and the action required if they occur;

(6) Techniques for self-monitoring drug therapy;

(7) Proper storage;

(8) Prescription refill information; and

(9) Action to be taken in the event of a missed dose.

f. Counseling is not required for inpatients of a hospital or institution where licensed healthcare practitioners are authorized to administer drugs (nursing homes, etc.).

g. Counseling is not required when a patient or caregiver refuses the offer or fails to respond to an offer. The failure to respond is deemed a refusal.

h. The pharmacist or designee must document when a patient or caregiver refuses counseling. The documentation must include the name or initials of the pharmacist or designee noting the refusal. Examples of documentation include a notation on the prescription, patient profile, or electronic record of the pharmacy, or a writing signed by the patient or caregiver.

4. Information gained by a pharmacist, pharmacy, or employee of a pharmacy about a patient from a patient profile or during a PDR or counseling is regarded as confidential. This information may only be revealed if the patient consents to the information being disclosed or if the information is required to be disclosed by a PBOP mandate, state or federal law, or a court order.
F. Sale of Hypodermic Needles (PBOP Rule 49 Pa. Code § 27.18(s))
   1. Sales of hypodermic needles and syringes are only allowed to be made by a pharmacist or by one delegated under the direct, immediate, and personal supervision of a pharmacist (e.g., pharmacy intern or technician).
   2. A prescription is not required to purchase hypodermic needles and syringes.
   3. Hypodermic needles and syringes shall be kept in the prescription area of the pharmacy, and be accessible only by pharmacists and pharmacy personnel authorized to be in the prescription area of the pharmacy while the pharmacy is open.

STUDY TIP: Syringes in Pennsylvania can be dispensed without a prescription, and there are no age or quantity limits imposed. However, the needles must be stored in and sold from a pharmacy.

G. Sale of Poisons (63 P. S. § 390-9)
   1. Pharmacies and pharmacists are permitted to sell certain poisons from the pharmacy if specific conditions are met.
   2. The PPA places poisons into either Schedule A or Schedule B. The PBOP has the authority to add or delete poisons from either schedule, and the PBOP is to keep a list of common antidotes.
      a. Schedule A poisons include:
         (1) Arsenic compounds and preparations.
         (2) Cyanides and preparations including hydrocyanic acid.
         (3) Fluorides soluble in water and preparations.
         (4) Mercury compounds and preparations (except preparations made and labeled for external use only and containing not more than 0.5% total mercury, and

except ointments or soaps containing not more than 2% total mercury or not more than 10% ammonium mercuric chloride or mercuric oxide).

(5) Phosphorous and preparations.

(6) Thallium compounds and preparations.

(7) Aconite, belladonna, cantharides, cocculus, conium, digitalis, gelsemium, hysocyamus, nux vomica, santonica, stramonium, strophanthus, veratrum, or their contained or derived active compounds and preparations (except preparations made and labeled for external use only, and except preparations containing not more than 0.004% total belladonna alkaloids, or not more than 0.02% total nux vomica alkaloids, and except preparations in dosage forms each containing not more than 2/10 milligram total belladonna alkaloids, or not more than 1 milligram total nux vomica alkaloids).

(8) Zinc phosphide and preparations.

(9) Sodium fluoroacetate and preparations.

b. Schedule B poisons include:

(1) Antimony, barium, copper, lead, silver, or zinc compounds soluble in water, and preparations containing 5% or more of these compounds.

(2) Bromine or iodine and preparations.

(3) Hypochlorous acid free or combined, and preparations that yield 10% or more of available chlorine, excepting chloride of lime or bleaching powder.

(4) Permanganates soluble in water and preparations containing 5% or more of these compounds.

(5) Nitric acid and preparations containing 5% or more of the free acid.

(6) Hydrochloric, hydrobromic or sulfuric acids, and preparations containing 10% or more of the free acids.

(7) Oxalic acid or oxalates, and preparations containing 10% or more of these compounds.

(8) Acetic acid, and preparations containing 20% or more of the free acid.

(9) Potassium or sodium hydroxides, and preparations containing 10% or more of the free alkalies.

(10) Ammonia solutions or ammonium hydroxide, and preparations containing 5% or more of free ammonia.

(11) Chloroform or ether, and preparations containing 5% or more of these compounds, except preparations made and labeled for external use only.

(12) Methyl alcohol or formaldehyde, and preparations containing 1% or more of these compounds, except when used as a preservative and not sold to the general public.

(13) Phenol or carbolic acid, cresole, or other phenol derivatives soluble in water, and preparations containing 5% or more of these compounds.

(14) Nitroglycerine and nitrites.

(15) Nicotine, and preparations containing nicotine expressed as alkaloid more than 2%.

(16) Ergot, cotton root, pennyroyal, and larkspur, or their contained or derived active compounds or mixtures thereof.

3. If a pharmacy or pharmacist wants to sell or provide a poison from Schedule A or B without obtaining a prescription for it, there must be a poison label on the package, box, or bottle that distinctly contains the word "poison" along with the name of the place of the seller, all in red ink. In addition, the label must contain the name of the poison in clear print.

4. Before selling or providing any poison in Schedule A or B an inquiry must be made to the person desiring it that they are aware of its poisonous character and that the poison is to be used for a legitimate purpose.

5. A poison in Schedule A and B cannot be sold, delivered, or provided to any person who is less than 16 years of age.

6. At the time of selling or providing any poison in Schedule A, an entry in a poison book kept solely for that purpose must occur. The entry is to state the date of sale, the name, address, and signature of the purchaser, the name and quantity of the poison sold, the statement of the purchaser of the purpose for which it is required, and the name of the dispenser, who shall be a registered pharmacist. This entry would not be required to be met when a pharmacist is

dispensing a poison pursuant to a prescription or when selling a poison to other pharmacists or medical practitioners.
7. A violation of this section constitutes a misdemeanor, which if found guilty includes a fine and potential prison time.

STUDY TIP: This section of the PPA covering poisons is an older section that may not commonly be used in today's practice environment. However, the language is still found within the law, and the MPJE has a competency statement regarding the dispensing of poisons.

H. Centralized Prescription Processing and Filling (PBOP Rule 49 Pa. Code § 27.203)
   1. Pennsylvania permits centralized prescription processing and filling. A review of the following definitions is important in understanding the different options that may be available:
      a. *Central fill pharmacy*—A pharmacy engaging in centralized prescription processing by filling and refilling prescriptions, which includes the preparation and packaging of the medication. A central fill pharmacy may also be the originating or delivering pharmacy.
      b. *Central processing center*—A pharmacy operated under the direction of a pharmacist that processes information related to the practice of pharmacy and that engages solely in centralized prescription processing but from which drugs are not dispensed.
      c. *Centralized prescription processing*—The processing, under the direction of a pharmacist, of a request to fill or refill a prescription, to perform functions such as refill authorizations, interventions, or other matters related to the practice of pharmacy for subsequent delivery to the delivering pharmacy.
      d. *Delivering pharmacy*—The pharmacy that receives the processed prescription or the filled or refilled prescription for delivery to the patient or the patient's authorized representative. A delivering pharmacy may also be an originating or central fill pharmacy.
      e. *Originating pharmacy*—The pharmacy that receives the patient's or prescribing practitioner's request to fill or refill a prescription and performs functions such as the prospective drug review. The term includes a central processing center or a central fill pharmacy if the

prescription was transmitted by the prescriber directly to the central processing center or central fill pharmacy or if the patient requested the refill from that pharmacy.

2. A central fill pharmacy or central processing center may fulfill a request for the processing, filling, or refilling of a prescription from either the originating pharmacy or from the patient or the prescriber and may deliver the processed, filled, or refilled prescription to a delivering pharmacy if the following requirements are met:

   a. The central fill pharmacy or the central processing center that is to process, fill, or refill the prescription has a contract with or has the same owner as the originating pharmacy and the delivering pharmacy. Contractual provisions must include confidentiality of patient information.

   b. The prescription container is clearly labeled with the information required by federal and state laws and regulations, and clearly shows the name, address, telephone number, and DEA number of the delivering pharmacy.

   c. Pharmacies that either utilize or act as central fill pharmacies or central processing centers must create operating policies and procedures. The policies and procedures must include an audit trail that records and documents the central prescription process and the individuals accountable at each step in the process for complying with federal and state laws and regulations including recordkeeping.

   d. Pharmacies that engage in centralized prescription processing share a common electronic file.

   e. Each pharmacy engaging in centralized prescription processing is jointly responsible for properly filling the prescription.

   f. The delivering pharmacy is responsible for making the offer to counsel to the patient.

   g. A pharmacy that serves as a central processing center is exempt from the requirement of maintaining an inventory of at least $5,000 worth of nonproprietary drugs and devices, the minimum size requirements for pharmacies, and the requirement to have a sink used solely for pharmaceutical purposes.

I. Technology and Automation (PBOP Rule 49 Pa. Code §§ 27.201–27.202)

   1. Electronically transmitted prescriptions must meet additional standards in addition to the standard information required on all other prescriptions (e.g., written or verbal).

      a. The following additional information is required:

         (1) A valid electronic signature of the prescriber.

         (2) The prescriber's telephone number.

         (3) The date of transmission.

         (4) The name of the pharmacy intended to receive the transmission.

      b. Electronic prescriptions must also meet the following standards:

         (1) The prescription must be electronically encrypted or transmitted by other technological means to protect and prevent access, alteration, manipulation, or use by any unauthorized person.

         (2) A hard copy or a readily retrievable image of the prescription information that is transmitted must be stored for at least 2 years from the date of the most recent filling.

         (3) For a pharmacy or pharmacist to accept the electronic transmission of a prescription for a Schedule II, III, IV, or V controlled substance, it must comply with all state and federal laws and rules.

         (4) The pharmacist and pharmacy may not provide electronic equipment to a prescriber for the purpose of transmitting prescriptions.

   2. Computerized systems used by a pharmacy for record-keeping and maintaining information concerning prescriptions must meet specific standards. These include:

      a. Provide immediate retrieval (by means of monitor, hard-copy printout, or other transfer medium) of patient information for all prescriptions filled within the previous 12 months.

    b. Provide retrieval of patient information within 3 working days for all prescriptions dispensed within the previous 24 months from the last activity date.

    c. The following data must be included in the retrieved patient information:

        (1) All federal and state information required to be on each prescription.

        (2) Identification of the pharmacist responsible for prescription information entered into the computer system.

    d. The system must be able to transfer all patient information to hard copy within 3 working days.

    e. Prescriptions entered into a computer system but not immediately dispensed must meet the following conditions:

        (1) The complete prescription information must be entered in the computer system.

        (2) The information must appear in the patient's profile.

        (3) The pharmacist who is responsible for the entry of the prescription must be identified in the computer system or on the hard copy of the prescription.

        (4) The original prescription must be filed properly.

        (5) If the computerized recordkeeping system experiences downtime, the prescription information must be entered into the computerized recordkeeping system as soon as it is available for use.

        (6) The system must have adequate safeguards to prevent access by any person who is not authorized to obtain information from the system, identify any modification or manipulation of information concerning a prescription, and prevent accidental erasure of information.

J. Automated Medication Systems (AMS) (PBOP Rule 49 Pa. Code § 27.204)

    1. The PBOP defines an AMS as a process that performs operations or activities, other than compounding or administration, relative to the storage, packaging, dispensing, and distribution of medications, and which collects, controls, and maintains all transaction information. The term does not include an automatic counting device or unit-based dispensing cabinet.

2. Automated medication systems may be used to store, package, dispense, or distribute prescriptions. For a pharmacy to use an automated medication system to fill prescriptions or medication orders, it must meet the following standards:

   a. If an AMS is used at an LTCF that does not have a pharmacy on-site, the pharmacist manager or pharmacist under contract with the LTCF is responsible for the supervision of the operation of the system.

   b. The AMS must have been tested and validated by the pharmacy as being able to accurately dispense prior to the implementation of the system. Test results must be provided to the PBOP upon request.

   c. The Board is permitted to access the AMS to validate the accuracy of the system.

   d. The AMS must electronically record the activity of each pharmacist, technician, or other authorized personnel with the time, date, and initials or other identifier so that a clear, readily retrievable audit trail is established. A pharmacist will be held responsible for transactions performed by that pharmacist or under the supervision of that pharmacist.

   e. The pharmacist manager or the pharmacist under contract with the LTCF responsible for the delivery of medications shall be responsible for the following:

      (1) Reviewing and approving all policies and procedures for system operation, safety, security, accuracy, access, and patient confidentiality.

      (2) Ensuring that medications in the AMS are inspected, at least monthly, for expiration date, misbranding, and physical integrity, and ensuring that the AMS is inspected, at least monthly, for security and accountability.

      (3) Assigning, discontinuing, or changing personnel access to the AMS.

      (4) Ensuring that the AMS is stocked accurately, and an accountability record is maintained in accordance with the written policies and procedures of operation.

      (5) Ensuring compliance with the applicable provisions of State and Federal law.

f. When an AMS is used to fill prescriptions or medication orders, it shall be operated according to written policies and procedures of operation created or adopted by the pharmacy. The policies and procedures of operation must:

(1) Include a table of contents.

(2) Include a description of all procedures of operation.

(3) Set forth methods that ensure retention of each amendment, addition, deletion, or other change to the policies and procedures of operation for at least 2 years after the change is made. Each change shall be signed or initialed by the registered pharmacist manager and include the date on which the registered pharmacist manager approved the change.

(4) Set forth methods that ensure that a pharmacist currently licensed in the transmitting jurisdiction reviews and approves the transmission of each original or new prescription or medication order to the automated medication system before the transmission is made.

(5) Set forth methods that ensure that access to the records of medications and other medical information of the patients maintained by the pharmacy is limited to licensed practitioners or personnel approved to have access to the records.

(6) Set forth methods that ensure that access to the automated medication system for stocking and removal of medications is limited to licensed pharmacists or the pharmacist's designee acting under the supervision of a licensed pharmacist. An accountability record which documents all transactions relative to stocking and removing medications from the AMS must be maintained.

(7) Identify the circumstances under which medications may be removed from the AMS by a licensed medical practitioner for distribution to a patient without prior order review by a licensed pharmacist.

g. A pharmacy that uses an AMS to fill prescriptions or medication orders shall review at least annually its written policies and procedures of operation and revise them, if necessary.

h. A copy of the adopted written policies and procedures of operation must be retained at the pharmacy and at the LTCF where the AMS is utilized. Upon request, the pharmacy shall provide to the PBOP a copy of the written policies and procedures of operation for inspection and review.

i. The pharmacist manager shall be responsible for ensuring that anyone performing any service in connection with the AMS is properly trained regarding it. The training shall be documented and available for inspection.

j. A pharmacy that uses an AMS to fill prescriptions or medication orders must create and operate under a written quality assurance program which:

(1) Requires monitoring of the AMS.

(2) Establishes mechanisms and procedures to test the accuracy of the AMS at least every 6 months and whenever any upgrade or change is made to the system.

(3) Requires the pharmacy to maintain all documentation relating to the quality assurance program for at least 2 years and provide this documentation to the PBOP upon request.

k. A pharmacy that uses an AMS must maintain a written plan for recovery from a disaster that interrupts the ability of the pharmacy to provide services. The written plan for recovery must include:

(1) Planning and preparation for a disaster.

(2) Procedures for response to a disaster.

(3) Procedures for the maintenance and testing of the written plan for recovery.

l. A pharmacy that uses an AMS must maintain a written program for preventative maintenance of the system. Documentation of completion of all maintenance shall be kept on file in the pharmacy for at least 2 years.

K. Return to Pharmacy Stock and Redistribution of Delivered and Undelivered Medications

1. Return to Stock and Redistribution of Delivered Medications (63 P. S. § 390-5(a)(9)(xi))

a. There are limited circumstances when a pharmacy may accept back dispensed medications from patients and then redistribute or reuse the medications for future prescriptions.

b. In general, an important rule to remember is that once a prescription medication is dispensed to a patient and the medication leaves the pharmacy, the pharmacy no longer has control over the medication. To accept the medication back and use it for future prescriptions could pose safety concerns. Therefore, in most instances, the medication cannot be returned and then reused.

c. The PPA states that the acceptance back and redistribution of any unused drug after it has left the premises of any pharmacy, whether issued by mistake or otherwise, is not permitted. However, the law does provide for an exception if the following circumstances are met:

(1) The medication is in the original sealed container with the name, lot number, and expiration date on the original intact manufacturer's label.

(2) The pharmacy is required to maintain records of all returns.

(3) A full refund shall be given to the original purchaser, including a third-party payor.
Note: While there is an exception to the law, in practice this may not occur, as many companies have policies prohibiting taking back and reusing any products once they have left the pharmacy. This is a good example to remember that, for the MPJE, you are being tested on the law, not company policies.

STUDY TIP: The general rule is that once a drug has been dispensed to a patient, it cannot be returned to be re-dispensed. The limited exception is also only for non-controlled drugs, as DEA does not permit this for controlled substances.

---

2. Return to Stock and Redistribution of Undelivered Medications (PBOP Policy Statement 49 Pa. Code § 27.102)

a. After a pharmacy has prepared or filled a prescription, there may be instances when the medication never gets picked up or delivered to the patient. When the prescription never leaves the control of the pharmacy, the PBOP allows these medications to be returned to active stock.

   b. The guidelines a pharmacy is to consider when returning undelivered medications to active stock to ensure the integrity of the drugs is maintained and patient safety is not compromised are listed here:

     (1) Prescriptions that have not been picked up by or delivered to the patient should be checked periodically.

     (2) The prescriptions never picked up/delivered should be assessed by a pharmacist to determine whether they might safely be returned to stock.

     (3) Products deemed eligible for re-dispensing should never be mixed within stock bottles of different lot numbers or with different expiration dates. Manufacturer's stock bottles should never be overfilled. The only safe manner in which drugs can be returned to stock bottles is in those pharmacies in which all medications are tracked by lot numbers and expiration dates.

     (4) In those instances in which medication cannot be properly and safely returned to the original stock bottle, the medication may be held in the pharmacy in the container in which it has been repackaged. It is recommended that pharmacies develop an internal manner for so identifying and dating these products.
Note: For pharmacies that don't track lot numbers and expiration dates, the medication may remain in the pharmacy vial.

     (5) Medications held for re-dispensing should be used as soon as possible. Medications held for re-dispensing that lack the original lot numbers and expiration dates should only be dispensed to patients up to 6 months from the date the drugs were first prepared for dispensing.

     (6) If the manufacturer or the FDA orders a recall for a drug product, pharmacists should assume products held in containers without lot numbers are included in the recall and proceed accordingly.

L. Other Rules Applicable to Pharmacies and/or Pharmacists

   1. A pharmacist may decline to fill or refill a prescription when a patient will not reimburse the pharmacist for the prescription. (PBOP Rule 49 Pa. Code § 27.18(c))

2. A pharmacist may decline to fill or refill a prescription if, in the pharmacist's professional judgment exercised in the interest of the safety of the patient, the pharmacist believes the prescription should not be filled or refilled. The pharmacist shall explain the decision to the patient. If necessary, the pharmacist shall attempt to discuss the decision with the prescriber. (PBOP Rule 49 Pa. Code § 27.18(c))

STUDY TIP: This PBOP rule would provide the pharmacist with the authority to decline to fill a prescription due to clinical concerns. This should only be done after consultation with the patient and/or prescriber.

3. The PBOP has provided guidance for pharmacists when one is religiously, morally, or ethically opposed to providing pharmaceutical services (e.g., compounding or dispensing certain prescriptions) that would reasonably be expected to be provided by pharmacists in meeting the needs of their patients. (PBOP Policy Statement 49 Pa. Code § 27.103)
   a. When a pharmacist recognizes that religious, moral, or ethical beliefs will result in the refusal to fill a prescription that is otherwise available in a pharmacy, the pharmacist has a professional obligation to take steps to avoid the possibility of abandoning or neglecting a patient. Pharmacists and pharmacies should consider the following guidelines when a pharmacist has a religious, moral, or ethical objection to filling certain prescriptions:
      (1) When a pharmacist begins practice in a professional setting, the pharmacist should take steps that may include notification to the owner and pharmacist manager if the pharmacist's beliefs will limit the drug products the pharmacist will dispense.
      (2) If a pharmacy employs a pharmacist that has identified circumstances that would preclude the filling of prescriptions for particular products, the owner and pharmacist manager should devise reasonable accommodations that will respect the pharmacist's choice while assuring delivery of services to patients in need. This may include the scheduling of pharmacists to allow a pharmacist who has a religious, moral, or ethical objection to practice simultaneously with another pharmacist who will fill the

requested prescription, entering into collaborative arrangements with pharmacies in close proximity, or other accommodations designed to protect the public.

(3) When a pharmacist has a religious, moral, or ethical objection to filling a prescription, the pharmacist should not interfere with another pharmacist responding to the professional needs of a patient. The objecting pharmacist should refrain from engaging in non-health related judgmental or confrontational activities with the patient.

(4) In the case of a pharmacy staffed by only one licensed pharmacist who conscientiously objects to performing certain pharmacy practices and providing services customarily and ordinarily performed by a licensed pharmacist at a pharmacy, the pharmacist should ensure that protocols are in place that will avoid results that cause harm or potential harm to any patients/customers as a consequence of any action or inaction by the pharmacist based upon any such conscientious objections, including, but not limited to, the denial of access to prescribed medications and disruptions in the continuity of care.

4. A pharmacist cannot enter into a paid or unpaid arrangement or agreement with a non-licensed person that would allow for prescription orders, prescription drugs, and/or devices to be regularly left with, picked up from, solicited by, accepted by, or delivered to the non-licensed person (PBOP Rule 49 Pa. Code § 27.18(e)). However, this restriction does not apply to the following situations in which a licensee is permitted to participate in:

a. A licensee is allowed to pick up a prescription or deliver a prescription drug or device, at the request of the patient, at the office of the prescriber or the home of the patient, at an institution in which a patient is confined, at another place as the patient designates for his safety and convenience, or by means of an employee, the mail, or by common carrier.

b. A licensee is also allowed to deliver naloxone to an identified employee of a Pennsylvania correctional facility, prison, jail, or residential drug treatment facility under a prescription and for an identified individual who is pending release or discharge from the correctional facility, prison, jail, or residential drug treatment facility.

5. Pharmacies, pharmacy owners, or pharmacist managers are not allowed to provide a prescriber with prescription blanks that contain the pharmacist's name or the name or address of the pharmacy on them. (PBOP Rule 49 Pa. Code § 27.18(q))

6. A patient has the right to request a copy of an original prescription. The copy must clearly indicate on its face that it is a copy and may not be used to obtain a new prescription or refill. Before a pharmacist provides a copy of a written prescription to a patient or the patient's agent, the person requesting the copy must show the pharmacist acceptable authorization and identification, such as a driver's license. The pharmacist must record in writing the date and to whom and by whom the copy was given. (PBOP Rule 49 Pa. Code § 27.18(r)(7))

7. Advertising the sale of drugs is permitted, but the following requirements must be met: (PBOP Rule 49 Pa. Code § 27.18(r))

    a. The advertising for filling or refilling of prescriptions for consumers or patients in Pennsylvania can only be done by pharmacies and/or pharmacists that are licensed by the PBOP.

    b. No person or pharmacy may promote to the public the sale of any controlled substances.

    c. Advertisements of prescription drugs and devices may not be false or misleading, and must be truthful, reasonable, informative, and understandable to the public.

    d. An advertisement for a prescription must be for a commercially reasonable quantity. If a person advertising special prices for prescriptions, prescription drugs, products, or devices desires to use a percentage number discount, such as 10% off select items, then the price list from which the percentage price is derived from must be stated or published so the patient knows exactly what the retail price is.

8. Prescriptions sent through the mail to a pharmacy shall be compounded and dispensed in the following manner: (PBOP Rule 49 Pa. Code § 27.18(l))

a. Prescription medications must be sent only in first class mail or common carrier, except where the purchaser is advised and agrees in advance that a slower means of transportation will be used.

b. The mailing of antibiotics which have been reconstituted is prohibited.

c. The mailing of a medication or prescription drug or device generally accepted and recognized to be subject to significant deterioration of the original content due to heat, cold fermentation, or prolonged agitation is permissible if it is shipped in a manner which would preserve the integrity of the drug, such as cold packs or other temperature control devices and sensors that would alert the patient if the integrity of the drug was compromised.

9. When other federal and state laws are violated by a pharmacy and/or pharmacist, including ones that involve pharmacy practice and consumer protection, this also constitutes a violation of the PPA and PBOP Rules. Examples include the FDCA, FCSA, PCSDDCA/PCSDDCR, and Pennsylvania Unfair Trade Practices and Consumer Protection Law (73 P. S. §§ 201-1–201-9.2). (PBOP Rule 49 Pa. Code §§ 27.18(r)(8), (u))
Note: This means it is possible that one act by a pharmacy or pharmacist could have multiple consequences. For example, if a pharmacist were to dispense a misbranded product, the pharmacist could face multiple charges and/or penalties, including from the FDCA and PCSDDCA/PCSDDCR, as well as the PPA/PBOP Rules.

10. The pharmacist has the responsibility to make their professional service available under the following conditions: (PBOP Rule 49 Pa. Code § 27.18(p))

a. A pharmacist practicing in a hospital, institution, or similar place or specialized ambulatory care unit may not be required to extend pharmaceutical services to other than registered patients of that hospital or institution.

b. A pharmacist shall offer complete pharmaceutical service by compounding or dispensing prescriptions which may reasonably be expected to be compounded or dispensed by pharmacists to meet the needs of persons who would usually attempt to utilize the services.

     c. No pharmacy or pharmacist may discriminate against a person on account of race, creed, religion, national origin, or sex.

11. When an oral prescription order is received by the pharmacist or pharmacy intern, it must be immediately reduced to writing. (PBOP Rule 49 Pa. Code § 27.18(o))

12. An order entered on the chart or medical record of a patient in an institution for the treatment of a patient on an overnight basis, or on the chart or medical record of a patient obtaining emergency treatment in a hospital, is considered a prescription if the medication will be furnished directly to the patient for self-administration. Since prescriptions have to meet additional requirements compared to medication orders, it is the responsibility of the prescriber to make sure the chart or medical record contains the required information. To dispense the medication, a pharmacist must first obtain an original prescription or a direct copy of it. (PBOP Rule 49 Pa. Code § 27.18(o))

13. Inspection reports by the PBOP must be kept on file at the pharmacy and be readily available upon request of the PBOP for at least 2 years from the date the report was issued. (PBOP Rule 49 Pa. Code § 27.13)

14. Pharmacies and pharmacists may accept faxed prescriptions as the original prescription for non-controlled prescription medications, and for controlled prescription medications under the same circumstances as permitted by federal law (*see Chapter 2, Sections VII.B. and VIII.A*). A pharmacist or pharmacy may not contribute to the installation of a fax machine in the office of any prescriber. (PBOP Rule 49 Pa. Code § 27.20)

III. **Drug Therapy Protocols and Collaborative Drug Therapy Management; Laboratory Waivers** (63 P. S. §§ 390-9.1, 390-9.3, and 390-9.5; PBOP Rule 49 Pa. Code §§ 27.301, 27.302, 27.311, and 27.312)

  A. Drug Therapy Protocols

    1. A pharmacist is permitted to enter into a written agreement or protocol with a licensed physician authorizing the management of drug therapy in an institutional setting.

    2. The licensed physician who enters a written agreement or protocol authorizing the management of drug therapy by a pharmacist shall be in active practice, and the written agreement or protocol must be within the scope of the licensed physician's current practice.

3. The management of drug therapy must be performed under a written agreement or protocol consistent with the institution's assignment of clinical duties. Ordering laboratory tests and ordering or performing other diagnostic tests necessary in the management of drug therapy must be consistent with the testing standards of the institution.

4. Participation in a written agreement or protocol authorizing the management of drug therapy shall be voluntary, and no licensed physician, pharmacist, or institution shall be required to participate.

5. A pharmacist that enters into a written agreement or protocol authorizing the management of drug therapy must obtain and maintain professional liability insurance coverage in the minimum amount of one million dollars ($1,000,000) per occurrence or claim made. Failure to maintain active coverage while participating in the management of drug therapy could result in the pharmacist being disciplined by the PBOP. The PBOP accepts purchased professional liability insurance, professional liability insurance coverage provided by the pharmacist's employer, or any similar type of coverage.

6. Written agreements or protocols must meet specific parameters. Written agreements or protocols must:

    a. Be in writing.

    b. Provide for notification of the role of the pharmacist by a licensed physician to each referred patient whose drug therapy management may be affected by the agreement. The patient has the opportunity to refuse management of drug therapy by a pharmacist.

    c. Be available as follows:
        (1) At the practice site of any licensed physician who is a party to the agreement.
        (2) At the practice site of any licensed pharmacist who is a party to the agreement.
        (3) At the institution where a written agreement or protocol is in place.
        (4) To any patient whose drug therapy management is affected by the agreement.

(5) Upon request, to representatives of the State Board of Medicine, the State Board of Osteopathic Medicine, the State Board of Pharmacy, and the Department of Health.

d. Identify, by name, each licensed physician and each licensed pharmacist who are parties to the agreement.

e. Be signed and dated by each licensed physician and each licensed pharmacist.

f. Specify the functions and tasks which are the subject of the written agreement or protocol, including:

(1) A statement requiring that regimens for the management of drug therapy be initiated by a physician for patients' referred to a pharmacist for management of drug therapy.

(2) A statement identifying the types of decisions regarding the management of drug therapy that the pharmacist is authorized to make, including a statement of the ailments or diseases involved within the physician's scope of practice, and types of management of drug therapy authorized.

(3) A statement of the functions and tasks the pharmacist shall follow in the course of exercising management of drug therapy, including the method for documenting decisions and a plan for communication or feedback to the authorizing physician as soon as practical, but no later than 72 hours after the intervention in the patient's medical record. The pharmacist is also to record this information in the pharmacist's records.

(4) A statement that requires notification to the authorizing physician of any changes in dose, duration, or frequency of medication prescribed as soon as possible, but no longer than 72 hours after the change.

g. Provide for execution of the agreement when any licensed physician or licensed pharmacist may be temporarily absent from a practice setting or temporarily unavailable to participate in its execution.

h. Be filed with the State Board of Pharmacy and the State Board of Medicine and/or the State Board of Osteopathic Medicine.

        i. Remain in effect for a period not to exceed 2 years, and every 2 years or sooner the parties shall review the agreement and make a determination as to its renewal, necessary modifications, or termination.

        j. Allow for termination of the agreement at the request of any party to it at any time.

  7. The management of drug therapy within an institution may occur without the requirements of 5.a.–j. listed above if it is pursuant to a medical order by a physician for managing drug therapy under a protocol approved by the medical staff of the institution.

     Note: When an institution has an institution-wide protocol in place for the management of drug therapy, when the physician within the institution issues a medical order for it, a separate written agreement or protocol meeting all the parameters listed above is not required.

B. Collaborative Drug Therapy Management

  1. A pharmacist is permitted to enter into a written collaborative agreement with a physician authorizing the management of drug therapy for a disease or for a condition or symptom of a disease in a practice setting other than an institutional setting.

  2. A pharmacist who is a party to a collaborative agreement authorizing the management of drug therapy must utilize an area for in-person, telephonic, or other approved electronic consultations relating to the management of drug therapy that ensures the confidentiality of the patient information being discussed.

  3. A pharmacist who is employed by a physician under a collaborative agreement for the purpose of management of drug therapy may not engage in retail dispensing while in the healthcare practice or within the context of employment.

  4. A pharmacist who is a party to a collaborative agreement authorizing the management of drug therapy must obtain and maintain a level of professional liability insurance coverage in the minimum amount of one million dollars ($1,000,000) per occurrence or claims made. Failure to maintain insurance coverage could lead to the pharmacist being disciplined by the PBOP. The pharmacist must provide an affidavit to the PBOP that they have obtained professional liability insurance. The PBOP accepts personal purchased liability insurance, professional liability insurance coverage provided by the individual licensee's employer, or similar insurance coverage.

5. A pharmacist may not provide economic incentives to a licensed physician for the purpose of entering into a collaborative agreement for the management of drug therapy.

6. The management of drug therapy under a collaborative agreement must be initiated by a written referral from the licensed physician to the pharmacist. The written referral shall include the frequency in which the pharmacist must conduct the management of drug therapy in person.

7. The licensed physician who is a party to the collaborative agreement authorizing the management of drug therapy must hold an active license in good standing and the terms of the collaborative agreement must be within the scope of the licensed physician's current practice.

8. Participation in a collaborative agreement authorizing the management of drug therapy must be voluntary, and no licensed physician or pharmacist shall be required to participate.

9. A patient's records related to the management of drug therapy may be maintained in a computerized recordkeeping system that meets all federal and state requirements for electronic health records.

10. A pharmacist who participates in a collaborative agreement authorizing the management of drug therapy must have access to the records of the patient who is the recipient of the management of drug therapy.

11. The handling of all patient records by the pharmacist providing the management of drug therapy must comply with HIPAA.

12. The collaborative agreement must be between a pharmacist and a physician.

13. The collaborative agreement must contain:
    a. A statement identifying the physician responsible for authorizing the management of drug therapy.
    b. A statement identifying the pharmacist authorized to perform the management of drug therapy.
    c. A statement requiring that regimens for the management of drug therapy be initiated by a physician for patients referred to a pharmacist for management of drug therapy.

d. A statement identifying the types of decisions regarding the management of drug therapy that the pharmacist is authorized to make within the physician's scope of practice and types of management of drug therapy authorized.

e. A statement identifying the terms under which a pharmacist providing the management of drug therapy is permitted to:

(1) Adjust the drug regimen, the drug strength, and the frequency of administration or the route of administration;

(2) Administer drugs;

(3) Order laboratory tests; and

(4) Order and perform other diagnostic tests necessary in the management of drug therapy without prior written or oral consent by the collaborating physician.

f. A statement of the functions and tasks the pharmacist shall follow in the course of exercising management of drug therapy, including the method for documenting decisions made and a plan for communication or feedback to the authorizing physician concerning specific decisions made. Documentation of each intervention shall occur as soon as practicable, but no later than 72 hours after the intervention, and be recorded in the pharmacist's records.

g. A statement that requires notification to the authorizing physician of changes in dose, duration, or frequency of medication prescribed as soon as practicable but no longer than 72 hours after the change.

h. A provision for implementation of the collaborative agreement when a physician or pharmacist who is a party to the agreement is temporarily unavailable to participate in its implementation.

i. A provision for notification of the role of the pharmacist by a physician to each referred patient, the management of whose drug therapy may be affected by the collaborative agreement, and providing an opportunity for the patient to refuse management of drug therapy by a pharmacist.

    j. The signatures of the physicians and pharmacists who are entering into the collaborative agreement and the dates signed.

    k. A statement allowing for the termination of the collaborative agreement at the request of a party to it at any time. *Note: When a pharmacist participates in a drug therapy protocol and/or collaborative drug therapy management, the pharmacist has NOT been granted prescriptive authority.*

14. The collaborative agreement must be available:

    a. At the practice site of each physician who is a party to the collaborative agreement.

    b. At the practice site of each pharmacist who is a party to the collaborative agreement.

    c. To any patient the management of whose drug therapy is affected by the agreement, upon request of the patient.

    d. Upon request, to representatives of the Pennsylvania licensing Boards (e.g., Pharmacy and Medicine), and the Department of Health.

15. The collaborative agreement shall be filed with the Pennsylvania Department of State (which the Boards of Pharmacy and Medicine are under).

16. The collaborative agreement must be maintained on the premises of the pharmacy for review during inspection by or upon request of representatives of the state, the PBOP, and the Department of Health.

17. The collaborative agreement must be effective for no more than 2 years from the date of execution. At the end of the 2-year period, or sooner, the parties must review the collaborative agreement and make a determination as to its renewal, necessary modifications, or termination.

18. A pharmacist who is party to a collaborative agreement authorizing the management of drug therapy shall:

    a. Utilize an area for in-person, telephonic, or other approved electronic consultations regarding the management of drug therapy that ensures the confidentiality of the patient information being discussed.

    b. Initiate the management of drug therapy only upon a written referral to the pharmacist from the physician. The written referral must include the minimum frequency in which the pharmacist shall conduct the management of the drug therapy in person.

   c. Confirm that the physician who is a party to the collaborative agreement holds an active and unrestricted license and that the terms of the collaborative agreement are within the scope of the physician's current practice at the time of the execution of the collaborative agreement.

19. Patient records regarding the management of drug therapy may be maintained in a computerized recordkeeping system which meets the federal and state requirements for electronic healthcare records, and is subject to the following:

   a. The pharmacist who is a party to the collaborative agreement shall have access to the records of the patient who is the recipient of the management of drug therapy.

   b. The physician who is a party to the collaborative agreement shall have access to the pharmacy records of the patient who is the recipient of the management of drug therapy.

   c. The handling of patient records by the pharmacist providing the management of drug therapy shall comply with HIPAA and the Health Information Technology for Economic and Clinical Health Act (Pub. L. No. 111-5, Div. A, Title XIII, Div. B, Title IV, 123 Stat. 226, 467), and associated rules and regulations.

C. Laboratory Tests

   1. The PPA was amended in 2020 to allow for a pharmacy or pharmacist to order and perform laboratory examinations and procedures for COVID-19, influenza, and streptococcal infections authorized or approved by the FDA under the Clinical Laboratory Improvement Amendments of 1988 (CLIA).

   2. The pharmacy needs to obtain a valid certificate of waiver (license) issued by the Centers for Medicare and Medicaid Services to order and perform the authorized laboratory examinations and procedures.

   Note: In general, facilities across the US that perform laboratory testing on human specimens for health assessment or the diagnosis, prevention, or treatment of disease are regulated under the Clinical Laboratory Improvement Amendments of 1988 (CLIA). Waived tests include test systems cleared by FDA for home use and those tests approved for waiver under the

CLIA criteria. Under this 2020 PPA amendment, pharmacies and pharmacists that obtain the required CLIA-waived lab license will be permitted to order and perform certain CLIA-waived tests (also referred to as "point-of-care testing").

IV. Pennsylvania Generic Equivalent Drug Law and Regulations
(35 P. S. §§ 960.1–960.7; PA Act 95 of 2016; 28 Pa. Code §§ 25.53–25.55)

A. Generic Equivalent Drugs and Interchangeable Biological Products

1. Pennsylvania law defines a "generically equivalent drug" as a drug product that the FDA has approved as safe and effective and has determined to be therapeutically equivalent, as listed in "The Approved Drug Products with Therapeutic Equivalence Evaluations" (FDA Orange Book), provided, however, that drug products found by the FDA to have a narrow therapeutic range (e.g., narrow therapeutic index (NTI) drugs) shall not be considered generically equivalent for the purposes of this act.

2. Pennsylvania law defines an "interchangeable biological product" as a biological product licensed by the FDA and determined to meet the safety standards for interchangeability pursuant to the Public Health Service Act (42 U.S.C. § 201 et seq.) or a biological product approved by the FDCA and determined by the FDA to be therapeutically equivalent to a prescribed biological product. For additional information regarding FDA interchangeability, *see Chapter x (K).*

3. A pharmacist is permitted to substitute a generic equivalent drug or interchangeable biological product for a prescribed brand product if it is listed as equivalent or interchangeable by the Pennsylvania Department of Health Formulary or by the FDA Orange Book or Purple Book.

STUDY TIP: Do not confuse generic substitution with therapeutic substitution, which is defined as the practice of replacing a patient's prescribed medicinal drug with another chemically different medicinal drug that is expected to have the same clinical effect. While this may occur in hospitals, it is typically not permitted in other practice settings.

Note: If a product is excluded or NOT listed by the Department of Health or FDA as equivalent or interchangeable, the pharmacist cannot substitute it. In practice, the Department of Health has not provided an updated formulary for a long time; however, it is still referenced in the law. Therefore, without an updated state formulary, pharmacists in Pennsylvania would then only refer to the Orange Book or Purple Book.

4. A pharmacist cannot substitute a generic drug for a prescribed brand name drug if the drug is considered an NTI drug.

STUDY TIP: Pennsylvania recognizes A-rated products in the Orange Book as generically equivalent. However, Pennsylvania excludes NTI drugs from the definition. This does not mean a pharmacist cannot substitute an NTI drug, however; rather, a pharmacist cannot automatically substitute an NTI drug without prescriber intervention. The pharmacist would need to take additional steps, such as discussing the matter with the prescriber.

B. Requirements and Restrictions to Substitution
1. Whenever a pharmacist receives a prescription for a brand name drug or biological product, the pharmacist *shall* substitute a less expensive generically equivalent drug or *may* substitute an interchangeable biologic unless requested otherwise by the purchaser or indicated otherwise by the prescriber.
   Note: Pennsylvania requires a pharmacist to dispense a generically equivalent drug unless requested by the patient or indicated by the prescriber. For an interchangeable biologic, the law states a pharmacist may substitute it.
2. For a Pennsylvania prescriber to indicate to the pharmacist on a written prescription to not dispense a generic equivalent drug or interchangeable biologic product, the following requirements must be met:
   a. The bottom of every prescription blank must be printed with the words "substitution permissible" and must contain one signature line above this wording for the prescriber's signature.
   b. The prescriber's signature validates the prescription.
   c. Under the prescriber's signature line, the following statement is to be printed: "In order for a brand name product to be dispensed, the prescriber must handwrite 'brand necessary' or 'brand medically necessary' in the space below."

   d. Unless the prescriber handwrites "brand necessary" or "brand medically necessary" in the space provided under the required statement, then the prescriber's signature on the signature line designates approval for a pharmacist to substitute a generic equivalent drug or interchangeable biological product for the brand name product.

   e. All information printed on the prescription blank shall be in 8-point uppercase print.

```
R   PATIENT'S
    NAME _____ AGE _____
    ADDRESS _____ DATE _____




    SUBSTITUTION PERMISSIBLE _____ M.D.
    IN ORDER FOR A BRAND NAME PRODUCT TO BE DISPENSED, THE PRESCRIBER MUST HAND
    WRITE "BRAND NECESSARY" OR "BRAND MEDICALLY NECESSARY" IN THE SPACE BELOW.
    _____
    OFFICE
    ADDRESS _____ DEA NO. _____
    REPETATUR  YES❑ NO❑  TIMES _____     PA LC NO. _____
                                                        ITEM #52925
```

3. For oral prescriptions, the pharmacist is not permitted to substitute a brand name product with a generic equivalent drug or interchangeable biological product if the prescriber expressly indicates to the pharmacist that the brand name product is necessary and substitution is not allowed.

4. For electronic prescriptions, the prescribing software/system being used should provide a way for the prescriber to communicate to the pharmacist that the brand name product is required to be dispensed or that substitution is prohibited. For example, in the "Comments to Pharmacist" field the prescriber could indicate that the brand name product is medically necessary.

C. Notification Requirements
   1. When the pharmacist is to substitute a less expensive generically equivalent or interchangeable product for a brand name product, notification to the person presenting the prescription must be made by the pharmacist or designee. Notification is to include advising the person presenting the prescription that a substitutable product is available, advising the person of the amount of the retail price difference between the brand name and substituted product, and informing the person that he/she may refuse the substitution.
   2. Notification to the individual can occur verbally or in writing.
   3. Every pharmacy must post in a prominent place that is in clear and unobstructed public view, at or near the place where prescriptions are dispensed, a sign which shall read as follows: "Pennsylvania law permits pharmacists to substitute a less expensive generically equivalent drug or interchangeable biological product for a brand name drug unless you or your physician direct otherwise." This sign must be printed in boldface letters not less than 1 inch or 2.54 centimeters in height on a white background.
   4. Every pharmacy must post in a conspicuous place, which is easily accessible to the general public, a list of commonly used generically equivalent drugs and interchangeable biological products containing the generic names and brand names.
   5. Every pharmacy must have available to the public a price listing of brand name and generic equivalent drug products and interchangeable biological products available at the pharmacy for selection by the purchaser.
      Note: The posting of the sign is still practiced. Although the posting of the lists and prices may not commonly be done by pharmacies, the requirement is still listed in the law and rules.
   6. When a mail order pharmacist is to substitute a less expensive generically equivalent drug or interchangeable biological product for a brand product by mail, the following requirements must be met:
      a. All communications the mail order pharmacy makes in connection with the solicitations of mail order customers, including direct mailings, general advertising, or on

order forms, must include notice in upper case letters and in boldface type as follows: "PENNSYLVANIA LAW PERMITS PHARMACISTS TO SUBSTITUTE A LESS EXPENSIVE GENERICALLY EQUIVALENT DRUG OR INTERCHANGEABLE BIOLOGICAL PRODUCT FOR A BRAND NAME DRUG UNLESS YOU OR YOUR PHYSICIAN DIRECT OTHERWISE"; "CHECK HERE IF YOU DO NOT WISH A LESS EXPENSIVE BRAND OR GENERIC/INTERCHANGEABLE PRODUCT."

b. After receiving a prescription order, a mail order pharmacy shall substitute a less expensive generically equivalent drug or interchangeable drug product unless expressly directed otherwise by the person presenting the prescription or the prescribing physician.

c. When a generically equivalent drug or interchangeable product is dispensed by mail, the pharmacy must notify the person presenting the prescription of the substitution and must indicate the retail price difference between the brand name drug and the generic equivalent drug product substituted for it.

7. Within 72 hours following the dispensing of an interchangeable biological product, the pharmacist or the pharmacist's designee must communicate to the prescriber the specific product provided to the patient, including the name of the product and the manufacturer. The communication is to be conveyed through an electronic records system accessible by the prescriber (e.g., entry in the patient's electronic health record or through an electronic prescribing technology). Otherwise, the pharmacist is to communicate the information by facsimile, telephone, electronic transmission, or other prevailing means. Notification or communication to the prescriber is not required when:

a. There is no FDA-approved interchangeable biological product for the product prescribed; or

b. It is a refill prescription and the interchangeable biological product dispensed is the same that was dispensed at the prior filling of the prescription.

8. Prescription refills must be filled using the identical product (same distributor and manufacturer) that was originally dispensed, unless the person presenting the prescription and

the prescriber authorize in advance a different manufacturer's generic equivalent or interchangeable product. Advance authorization is not required in an emergency, but the prescriber must be notified by the pharmacist as soon as possible thereafter.

D. Additional Requirements

  1. Any questions by the person presenting the prescription for drug product information must be answered only by the pharmacist or pharmacy intern.

  2. Substitution of a less expensive generically equivalent drug is contingent on whether the pharmacy has the brand name or generically equivalent drug in stock.

  3. Any pharmacist substituting a less expensive generic equivalent drug or interchangeable biological product must charge the purchaser the regular and customary retail price for the product.

    Note: In today's practice environment, most prescriptions are covered by insurance, and the pricing is already determined. However, for cash-paying customers this requirement would apply.

  4. Each pharmacist must maintain a record of any substitution of a generically equivalent drug or interchangeable biological product for a prescribed brand name drug.

  5. When a pharmacist complies with the Pennsylvania Generic Equivalent Drug Law, he/she will not be liable in any way for the dispensing of a generically equivalent drug or interchangeable biological product unless the product was incorrectly substituted.

  6. A prescriber will not be liable for any actions arising from the use of the substituted product by the pharmacist unless the original drug was incorrectly prescribed.

E. Narrow Therapeutic Index (NTI) Drugs

  1. The Pennsylvania Department of Health has provided guidance on the generic substitution of NTI drugs. The guidance provides the following information:

    a. The automatic substitution by a pharmacist of a generic for a brand name is prohibited when a physician prescribes a brand name product and the generic drug is determined to be an NTI drug, non-A rated, or the physician writes "brand necessary."

b. Pennsylvania law states that an NTI drug is not substitutable regardless of bioequivalency rating in the Orange Book or safety/efficacy data; therefore, if a drug is determined to be an NTI drug it is not substitutable in Pennsylvania.

c. A current listing of NTI drugs is neither published/provided by the FDA or Pennsylvania.

d. Practitioners should utilize a variety of resources as well as their professional training to determine whether a particular drug is an NTI drug. Some examples of resources available in addition to their professional training are:

(1) A 1988 listing of NTI drugs published by the FDA. *See below*

(2) Legal Definition of NTI in the CFR, which provides that a "narrow therapeutic ratio" is defined as:

(i) less than a twofold difference in median lethal dose (LD50) and median effective dose (ED50) values, or

(ii) there is less than a twofold difference in the minimum toxic concentrations and minimum effective concentrations in the blood, and

(iii) safe and effective use of the drug products requires careful titration and patient monitoring.

(3) FDA-approved manufacturer package insert of drug or contact the manufacturer directly for information (NTI information is usually listed under "precautions").

(4) For generic substitutions not involving NTI drugs, practitioners should refer to the Orange Book to determine if a drug is A-rated.

(5) A sample list of NTI drugs published by the FDA in 1988; however, since this list is from 1988, a practitioner should still verify if the product is an NTI drug. Examples from the list include: aminophylline, carbamazepine, clindamycin, clonidine, digoxin, disopyramide, dyphylline, guanethidine, isoetharine mesylate, isoproterenol, levothyroxine, lithium carbonate, metaproterenol, minoxidil, oxytriphylline, phenytoin, prazosin, primidone, procainamide, quinidine, theophylline, valproic acid, valproate sodium, and warfarin.

V. Hospital Pharmacies and LTCFs (28 Pa. Code §§ 113.1–113.30)
    A. Rules Applicable to Hospital Pharmacies
        1. The Pennsylvania Department of Health has passed regulations that apply to hospital pharmacies providing pharmaceutical services.
        2. Hospitals must provide for pharmaceutical services which meet accepted ethical and professional practices.
        3. The scope of the pharmaceutical services in a hospital shall be consistent with the medication needs of the patients. Hospital pharmaceutical policies are to include a program for the control and accountability of drug products throughout the hospital.
        4. A hospital using an outside pharmacist or pharmaceutical service must have a contract with that pharmacist or service. As part of the contract, the pharmacist or service is required to maintain at least the standards for operation of the pharmaceutical services outlined in the Department of Health Rules.
        5. The following requirements apply to hospital pharmacists:
            a. When a hospital has a pharmacy, it must be directed by a licensed pharmacist.
            b. When a hospital does not have a pharmacy or full-time staff pharmacist, a consulting or part-time pharmacist shall have responsibility for the dispensing of drugs as well as the pharmaceutical functions of nursing stations.
            c. Pharmacists must be trained in the specialized functions of hospital pharmacy.
            d. Pharmacists are responsible to the chief executive officer or his designee for developing, supervising, and coordinating all the activities of the pharmacy.
            e. In the absence of a pharmacist, the dispensing of drugs shall be limited to emergencies and can only be performed under the direct supervision of a practitioner licensed under state law to prescribe and dispense drugs.
            f. The pharmacist must be assisted by an adequate number of additional pharmacists and such other personnel as the activities of the pharmacy may require to ensure adequate pharmaceutical services.

6. Hospitals must have a pharmacy and therapeutics (P&T) committee which includes physicians, nurses, and pharmacists. The P&T committee must do the following:

   a. Meet at least quarterly, record its proceedings, and report to the medical staff.

   b. Assist in the formulation of broad professional policies regarding the evaluation, appraisal, selection, procurement, storage, distribution, use and safety procedures, and all other matters relating to drugs in the hospital. This should include some mechanism to review and evaluate adverse drug reactions and make appropriate recommendations if necessary.

   c. Develop written policies and procedures pertaining to the intra-hospital drug distribution system. In developing such policies, the committee shall utilize, as necessary, representatives of other disciplines within the hospital.

   d. Serve as an advisory group to the hospital medical staff and the pharmacist on matters pertaining to the choice of drugs.

   e. Develop and review periodically a formulary or drug list for use in the hospital.

   f. Recommend standards regarding the use and control of investigational drugs and concerning research in the use of recognized drugs.

   g. Evaluate clinical data concerning new drugs or preparations requested for use in the hospital.

   h. Make recommendations concerning drugs to be stocked on the nursing unit floors and by other services.

   i. Establish procedures which will prevent unnecessary duplication in stocking drugs and drugs in combination having identical amounts of the same therapeutic ingredients.

   j. Make recommendations concerning drugs for which automatic stop drug orders are necessary.

   k. Make recommendations regarding proper procedures and policies on the administration of drugs.

7. Pharmacy facilities in hospitals must meet the following standards:

   a. Provide equipment and supplies for the pharmaceutical service to carry out its professional and administrative functions and to ensure patient safety through the proper storage and dispensing of drugs. Facilities shall be provided for the storage, safeguarding, preparation, and dispensing of drugs.

    b. Maintain a supply of drugs and devices adequate to meet the needs of the patients and the medical staff, including those required by the PBOP.

    c. Have storage cabinets in all areas of the hospital where drugs are stored, where pharmacists have control over all floor stocks and are required to periodically check the cabinets as determined by the P&T committee.

8. Hospital pharmacies have recordkeeping requirements.

    a. All drug transactions of the pharmacy must be recorded, and those records are to be kept with other hospital records. Recordkeeping requirements must also be met for other state and federal laws.

    b. The pharmacy must establish and maintain a system of records and bookkeeping that meets the policies of the hospital in order to maintain adequate control over the handling, dispensing, and billing for all drugs and supplies.

9. Records for drugs dispensed from the pharmacy must be maintained in the pharmacy, and records of drugs administered to patients must be maintained in the medical record of the patient.

10. Oral orders for medication or treatment are to only be accepted under urgent circumstances when it is impractical for the orders to be given in a written manner by the prescriber. Oral orders must also meet the following requirements: *See 28 Pa. Code § 107.62*

    a. Oral orders are only permitted to be taken by qualified personnel, and must meet the medical staff bylaws regarding who can transcribe and document the orders in medical records.

    b. The order shall include the date, time, and full signature of the person taking the order and shall be countersigned by a prescriber within 24 hours.

    c. If the prescriber is not the attending physician, he must be authorized by the attending physician and must be knowledgeable about the patient's condition.

    d. The medical staff bylaws must specify personnel who are qualified to accept oral orders and that acceptance of orders is limited to personnel listed in this subsection. Oral orders for medication are restricted to:

      (1) A practitioner.

      (2) A professional nurse.

      (3) A licensed practical nurse.

      (4) A pharmacist who may transcribe oral orders pertaining to drugs.

11. Copies of records of all adverse drug reactions and drug sensitivities must be maintained in the pharmacy for 2 years.

12. The label of each patient's individual medication container must provide the information required by the PBOP, PCSDDCA, and PCSDDCR. *See Section II. B.*

13. The hospital must have a drug formulary or list of drugs accepted for use in the hospital, which is to be developed and amended at regular intervals by the pharmacist and the appropriate committee.

14. The P&T committee, in cooperation with representatives of other disciplines as necessary, is to develop written policies and procedures governing the safe administration of drugs in the hospital. Such policies and procedures shall be approved by the governing body of the hospital. The policies and procedures regarding safe administration of drugs are to include the following:

    a. Establish controls governing the administration of dangerous drugs.

    b. Dangerous drugs include controlled substances, sedatives, anticoagulants, antibiotics, oxytoxics, and corticosteroids.

    c. Establish appropriate dosage and duration of order of dangerous drugs.

    d. Automatic stop procedures for dangerous drugs not specifically prescribed as to time or number of doses.
    Note: The medical staff is to establish a written policy for all dangerous drugs not specifically prescribed as to time or number of doses to be automatically stopped after a reasonable time limit. The prescriber also must be notified of the policies within 48 hours before an order is automatically stopped. 28 Pa. Code § 107.65.

15. The hospital must provide emergency pharmaceutical services. A secure emergency medication kit, stocked and approved by the pharmacist, must be kept readily available and under the control of either the pharmacy, a practitioner licensed by law to prescribe or dispense drugs, or, during emergency periods, a staff member designated by the chief executive officer or his designee.

16. Drugs, devices, and cosmetics under the control of the pharmacist which are outdated, visibly deteriorated, unlabeled, or inadequately labeled, recalled, discontinued, or obsolete shall be identified by the pharmacist and shall be disposed of in compliance with applicable state and federal laws and regulations.

17. If there is reason to suspect mishandling of scheduled or controlled drugs, the hospital administration must contact the Pennsylvania Bureau of Drug Control of the Office of the Attorney General.

B. Rules Applicable to Long Term Care Nursing Facilities (LTCFs) (28 Pa. Code § 211.9)

1. LTCFs in Pennsylvania have to comply with state Department of Health nursing home regulations. Various rules apply to pharmacy services in facilities; some/many applicable to pharmacy practice are provided below.

2. LTCFs are to have policies that ensure the following:
   a. Facility staff involved in the administration of resident care shall be knowledgeable of the policies and procedures regarding pharmacy services including medication administration.
   b. Only licensed pharmacists shall dispense medications for residents. Licensed physicians may dispense medications to the residents who are in their care.

3. Each resident must have a written physician's order for each medication (prescription and nonprescription) received.

4. Residents are permitted to purchase prescribed medications from the pharmacy of their choice. If the resident does not use the pharmacy that usually services the facility, the resident is responsible for securing the medications and for ensuring that applicable pharmacy regulations and facility policies are met. The facility:
   a. Must notify the resident or the resident's responsible person, at admission and as necessary throughout the

resident's stay in the facility, of the right to purchase medications from a pharmacy of the resident's choice as well as the resident's and pharmacy's responsibility to comply with the facility's policies and state and federal laws regarding packaging and labeling requirements.

    b. Must have procedures for receipt of medications from outside pharmacies including requirements for ensuring accuracy and accountability. Procedures are to include the review of medications for labeling requirements, dosage, and instructions for use by licensed individuals who are authorized to administer medications.

    c. Must ensure that the pharmacist or pharmacy consultant will receive a monthly resident medication profile from the selected pharmacy provider.

    d. Must have a policy regarding how to obtain medications in urgent situations. Facilities may order a 7-day supply from a contract pharmacy if the resident's selected pharmacy is not able to comply with this requirement.

5. If over-the-counter drugs are maintained in the facility, the drugs must be labeled with the original label and have the name of the resident on the label of the container. The charge nurse may record the resident's name on the nonprescription label. The use of nonprescription drugs is limited by quantity and category according to the needs of the resident. Facility policies must indicate the procedure for handling and billing of nonprescription drugs.

6. If a unit of use or multiuse systems are used, federal and/or state laws and rules that apply to their use must be met. Unit of use dispensing containers or multiuse cards must be properly labeled. Individually wrapped doses must be stored in the original container from which they were dispensed.

7. At least quarterly, outdated, deteriorated, or recalled medications in the facility must be identified and returned to the dispensing pharmacy for proper disposal. Written documentation by the facility must be kept regarding the transfer, distribution, and/or disposal of medications.

8. Properly disposing of discontinued and unused medications, as well as medications of discharged or deceased residents, must be handled by facility policy, which is to be developed in cooperation with the consultant pharmacist. The method of disposal and quantity of drugs are to be documented in

the resident's chart. The disposal procedures must be done at least quarterly and comply with state and federal laws.

9. The oversight of pharmaceutical services is the responsibility of the facility's quality assurance committee. The pharmacist responsible for the adequacy and accuracy of the pharmacy services to the facility must have committee input. The quality assurance committee, with input from the pharmacist, must develop written policies and procedures for drug therapy, distribution, administration, control, accountability, and use.

10. A facility must have at least one emergency medication kit. The kit used in the facility must meet the following requirements:

   a. The facility must have written policies and procedures regarding the use, content, storage, and refill of the kits.

   b. The quantity and categories of medications and equipment in the kits are to be kept to a minimum and must be based on the immediate needs of the facility.

   c. The emergency medication kits must be under the control of a practitioner authorized to dispense or medications under the PPA.

   d. The kits must be kept readily available to staff and must have a breakaway lock which is to be replaced after each use.

STUDY TIP: An emergency medication kit in a nursing home is one of the rare exceptions when DEA allows non-dispensed (or bulk) controlled substances to be stored at a location that does not have a DEA registration.

VI. Disciplinary Matters

A. The PBOP currently grants state licenses, permits, and registrations to pharmacies, pharmacists, and pharmacy interns. Additional state agencies, such as the Department of Health, also have oversight of pharmacies and pharmacists. When an individual or entity does not comply with the laws, rules, and practice standards one is required to meet, disciplinary proceedings and actions could occur. The following sections provide details regarding disciplinary matters, including the proceedings, potential actions by the PBOP, and circumstances that may lead to discipline.

Note: Other sections of this book have already listed various circumstances that could lead to discipline of a pharmacy, pharmacist, or pharmacy intern. In addition, once the PBOP passes regulations regarding pharmacy technicians, technicians will also be subject to disciplinary actions.

B. The PBOP can refuse to issue a license or discipline a current pharmacist's license when the pharmacist: (63 P. S. § 390-5(a))

    1. Procured a personal license through fraud, misrepresentation, or deceit.

    2. Has been found guilty, pleaded guilty, entered a plea of no contest, received probation without a verdict, or entered an Accelerated Rehabilitative Disposition (ARD) program for any offense in connection with the practice of pharmacy or any offense involving moral turpitude before any court of record of any jurisdiction.

    3. Is unfit to practice pharmacy because of the use of alcohol, controlled substances, or any other substance which impairs the intellect and judgment to such an extent as to impair the performance of professional duties.

    4. Is unfit or unable to practice pharmacy because of a physical or mental disease or disability.

        a. In enforcing this, the PBOP has authority to require a pharmacist to submit to a mental or physical examination by physicians or psychologists approved by the PBOP.

        b. Failure of a pharmacist to submit to an examination is considered an admission of the allegations against them, and a decision by the PBOP on the matter can be made without allowing for testimony or evidence by the pharmacist.

        c. A pharmacist impacted by this section must, at reasonable intervals, be provided an opportunity to demonstrate that he or she can resume a competent practice of pharmacy with reasonable skill and safety to patients.

    5. Has had a license to practice pharmacy issued by any other state suspended or revoked.

    6. Has violated or knowingly permitted the violation of any section of the PPA or PBOP.

    7. Has knowingly allowed any unlicensed person to take charge of a pharmacy or engage in the compounding, distribution, or dispensing of prescriptions or controlled substances. This section does not apply to the delegation of authorized activities of pharmacy interns or technicians when done under the direct and immediate personal supervision of a pharmacist.

8. Has compounded, dispensed, or sold any drug or device which contains more or less than the ingredients specified, or was a different product than what was prescribed, unless the consent of the prescriber was first obtained. This section does not apply to:
   a. Inert ingredients required to prepare the product;
   b. Reductions in quantities dispensed due to limits by insurance plans; or
   c. Products where the pharmacist properly substituted a generically equivalent drug or interchangeable biologic.

9. Is guilty of grossly unprofessional conduct. The following acts by a pharmacist have been determined to constitute grossly unprofessional conduct of a pharmacist:
   a. Intentionally deceiving or attempting to deceive the PBOP or its agents with respect to any material matter under investigation by the Board.
   b. Advertising of prices for drugs and pharmaceutical services to the public which does not conform to federal laws or regulations.
   c. Making public claims or implying that the pharmacist is superior in the practice of pharmacy as compared to other pharmacists.
   d. Engaging in untrue, false, misleading, or deceptive advertising of drugs or devices.
   e. Paying rebates to medical providers (e.g., physicians), or entering into any agreement with a medical provider for any payment or compensation for recommending the professional services of either party.
   f. Entering into any agreement with a prescriber for the compounding or dispensing of secret formula prescriptions.
   g. The misbranding or adulteration of any drug or device and the sale, distribution, or dispensing of any misbranded or adulterated drug or device.
   h. Engaging in the sale or purchase of drugs or devices whose package bears the inscription "sample" or "not for resale."

i. Displaying or allowing the display of the pharmacist's license in a pharmacy of which the pharmacist is not the proprietor or employed at.

j. Any holder of a biennial pocket registration card who fails to have the card available for inspection by an authorized agent while practicing.

k. The acceptance back and redistribution of any unused drug after it has left the premises of any pharmacy, unless specific conditions are met. *See Chapter 4, Section II.K.*

l. Accepting employment or receiving compensation as a pharmacist where any medical practitioner (or company they are involved with) has sufficient beneficial interest that allows them to exercise supervision or control over the pharmacist in his/her professional responsibilities and duties.
Note: There is an exception to this section that allows a pharmacist to be employed by a physician and receive appropriate compensation for the purpose of the management of drug therapy. However, the pharmacist cannot engage in retail dispensing related to this employment.

m. Accepting employment or compensation as a pharmacist from any person who orders the pharmacist, directly or indirectly, to engage in any aspect of the practice of pharmacy that contradicts any requirements of the PPA.

n. Entering into an arrangement with a prescriber for the purpose of directing patients to or from a specified pharmacy or restraining a patient's freedom of choice to select a pharmacy.
Note: This section does not prohibit a pharmacist from entering into a written agreement or written collaborative agreement with a licensed physician which authorizes the management of drug therapy.

10. Has had a license to practice pharmacy suspended, revoked, or refused, or has received other disciplinary action by the proper pharmacist licensing authority of another state, territory, or country.

11. Has acted in such a manner as to present an immediate and clear danger to the public health or safety.

12. Is guilty of incompetence, gross negligence, or other malpractice, or the pharmacist does not meet the standards of acceptable and prevailing pharmacy practice, in which case actual injury need not be established.

    Note: The language in the above section is broad and would allow for acts that are not specifically listed in the law and rules to also be considered violations of the PPA. When something would be against practice standards, it would also violate the PPA.

C. The PBOP can refuse or discipline a pharmacy's permit when: (63 P. S. § 390-5(b))

   1. The permit was obtained through fraud, misrepresentation, or deceit.
   2. Any holder of the permit has violated any federal or state law related to pharmacy, or has ordered a pharmacist it employs to engage in any aspect of the practice of pharmacy that contradicts any federal or state law related to pharmacy.
   3. Any holder of the permit has sold, caused, or allowed anyone other than a pharmacist to dispense any controlled substance or prescription drug.
   4. Any holder of the permit fails to continue to comply with all the requirements to conduct a pharmacy.
   5. The permit holder had knowledge or should have known of the illegal acts of a pharmacist it employed, and that pharmacist had their license suspended or revoked due to such illegal act.
   6. A pharmacist or pharmacy permit holder entered into an agreement with a prescriber for the purpose of directing patients to or from a specified pharmacy or restraining in any way a patient's freedom of choice to select a pharmacy.
   7. The pharmacy's permit to conduct a pharmacy or a non-resident pharmacy issued by another state licensing authority has been revoked or suspended or the pharmacy was otherwise disciplined.

D. When the PBOP determines that a pharmacist's license or pharmacy's permit should be disciplined, the Board may:

   1. Deny the application for a license or permit.
   2. Administer a public reprimand and/or fine the license or permit.
   3. Limit or otherwise restrict a license or permit.
   4. Place the license or permit on probation.

5. Suspend the license or permit.
6. Revoke the license or permit.
7. Require a licensee to submit to the care, counseling, or treatment of a physician or a psychologist designated by the Board.
8. Suspend enforcement of its finding and place a licensee on probation with the right to vacate the probationary order for noncompliance.
9. Restore or reissue, in its discretion, a suspended license to practice pharmacy and impose any disciplinary or corrective measure which it might originally have imposed.

E. Any person that had a license or registration suspended or revoked because of a felony conviction under state or federal controlled substance laws may apply for reinstatement after a period of at least ten years has elapsed from the date of conviction. The PBOP may reinstate the license if the Board is satisfied that the following conditions have been met:
1. The person has made significant progress in personal rehabilitation since the conviction.
2. The reinstatement should not be expected to create a substantial risk of harm to the health and safety of his or her patients or the public.
3. The reinstatement should not be expected to create a substantial risk of further criminal violations.
4. The person meets all other licensing qualifications of this PPA.
   Note: For revoked licenses that did not occur due to circumstances listed in the above section, the time limit for the Board to consider reinstatement is 5 years. See 63 P. S. § 390-7.1. Also, when a license or registration has been suspended or revoked, it must be returned to the PBOP. Failure to return the license or registration is a misdemeanor in the third degree.

F. Hearings and Suspensions (63 P. S. § 390-7)
1. When the PBOP refuses to issue any license, permit, registration, or certificate, it must give written notice, the reasons supporting the decision, and the opportunity for a hearing.
   a. Written notice by the PBOP must be given to the applicant personally or by registered or certified mail.
   b. After receiving the notice of refusal, the applicant has 15 days to submit in writing to the Board a request for a hearing.

2. The PBOP has the authority to investigate concerns arising regarding licensees and permittees.
    a. The PBOP must promptly investigate any alleged violations after receiving a complaint in writing regarding the wrongful acts of any licensee or permittee.
    b. The PBOP has the authority to suspend or permanently revoke licenses or permits at any time when, after due proceedings, it finds the licensee or permittee guilty of any violation of the PPA or PBOP rules.
3. Any hearings, appeals, and rulings under this section must be done following Pennsylvania Administrative Agency Law.
    a. A majority of the PBOP must designate the member or members to be present at each hearing.
    b. After each hearing, the notes of testimony are to be transcribed and a copy of the transcript must be given to each member of the PBOP who shall review the transcript prior to voting on the matter.
    c. All decisions by the PBOP must be reached by a majority vote of the entire Board.
    d. The PBOP must keep records of its decisions.
    e. The PBOP must give immediate notice, in writing, of any ruling or decision to the licensee or permittee impacted, and the date when the ruling or decision will become effective.
    f. When any discipline becomes final (e.g., revocation, suspension), the PBOP must publish the final decision.
        Note: The Pennsylvania Department of State website publishes a monthly list of disciplinary or corrective measures taken by all the state's professional licensing boards, including the PBOP. Each listing includes the name of the individual or entity, the associated license or permit number, the business address, the sanction imposed, a brief description of the basis for the discipline, and the effective date. In addition, the Pennsylvania Department of State also allows a search tool for the public to verify the professional license of an individual or entity. If there has been discipline against the person or entity, this database would also likely contain the publicly available documents associated with the discipline.

4. A license may be temporarily suspended under circumstances that were determined by the PBOP to be an immediate and clear danger to the public health and safety.

   a. The PBOP must issue an order for the temporary suspension without a hearing, but provide written notice to the licensee impacted along with the allegations.

   b. Temporary suspensions do not have to meet the Pennsylvania Administrative Agency Law requirements for regular proceedings.

   c. After issuing the temporary suspension and providing written notice to the licensee, the PBOP must initiate a formal action to suspend, revoke, or restrict the license.

   d. All actions by the PBOP must be taken promptly and without delay.

   e. Within thirty days after the issuance of an order temporarily suspending a license, the Board must conduct a preliminary hearing to determine that there is enough evidence at that time to support the temporary suspension.

   f. The licensee whose license has been temporarily suspended may be present at the preliminary hearing and may be represented by counsel, cross-examine witnesses, inspect physical evidence, call witnesses, offer evidence and testimony, and make a record of the proceedings.

   g. If it is determined that there is not enough evidence at that time to support the temporary suspension, the suspended license shall be immediately restored.

   h. A temporary suspension will remain in effect until the PBOP ends the suspension, but the maximum time frame for a temporary suspension to be in effect cannot be longer than 180 days.

5. A license must be automatically suspended when a licensee is legally committed to an institution because of mental incompetency, when the licensee has been convicted of a felony related to controlled substances, or convicted of a similar offense under a law in another jurisdiction. Restoration of any license automatically suspended must meet the same requirements for reinstatement that revoked or suspended licenses must meet.

G. Professional Impairment Program

    1. The PBOP appoints and compensates a professional consultant that is educated in and has experience with the identification, treatment, and rehabilitation of individuals with physical or mental impairments.

    2. The consultant is a liaison between the PBOP and treatment programs, including drug and alcohol treatment programs licensed by the Pennsylvania Department of Health, psychological counseling, and impaired professional support groups approved by the Board that provide services to licensees under the PPA.

    3. The PBOP may delay and eventually dismiss any of the types of corrective action or discipline that were initiated for an impaired professional as long as the professional is progressing satisfactorily in a PBOP-approved treatment program. However, this section does not apply to a professional/licensee that has been convicted of or pleaded guilty to a felony involving a controlled substance in any court.

    4. When an impaired professional enters an agreement for treatment, the program will provide the necessary information to the consultant which is the liaison to the PBOP. This applies to professionals who voluntarily enter a treatment program under a Board agreement, those under Board investigation, or those that entered a program voluntarily not under a Board agreement but that fail to adhere to or complete the program.

    Note: In Pennsylvania, Secundum Artem Reaching Pharmacists with Help (SARPH) is the liaison approved by the PBOP to assist pharmacists and pharmacy interns in managing substance abuse and mental health disorders. One of the goals of SARPH is to assist the professional in the recovery process and eventual safe return to practice. To learn more about the variety of services SARPH provides, refer to www.SARPH.org.

    5. When an impaired professional enrolls in an approved treatment program and enters an agreement with the PBOP, the pharmacist's or pharmacy intern's license will be suspended or revoked but enforcement of the suspension or revocation will be delayed for the time the professional is successfully progressing in the program.

    6. Failure to enter into an agreement for treatment will disqualify the professional from the impaired professional program and will result in an immediate investigation and disciplinary proceeding by the Board.

7. If the consultant has determined that the impaired professional enrolled in a treatment program has not satisfactorily progressed, the consultant is to disclose this to the PBOP, which will then begin proceedings to determine if the delay of enforcement of the discipline against the professional should end.

8. Any hospital, healthcare facility, peer, or colleague who has substantial evidence that a professional has an active addictive disease for which the professional is not receiving treatment, is diverting a controlled substance, or is mentally or physically incompetent to carry out the duties of his/her license is required to make a report to the PBOP. However, individuals or facilities in an approved treatment program treating the professional are exempt from this mandatory reporting requirement.

9. Any person or facility who reports the required information to the PBOP in good faith and without malice is immune from any civil or criminal liability arising from the report.

10. Failure to provide a required report within a reasonable time from knowledge of the impairment will result in a fine (not to exceed $1,000) against the person or facility. The Board will provide the person or facility the opportunity for a hearing.

STUDY TIP: The above provides for the mandatory reporting requirements for Pennsylvania, as well as the penalty for failure to report.

H. Unlawful Acts (63 P. S. § 390-8)
1. The PPA contains a section that lists unlawful acts related to the practice of pharmacy. Numerous items on this list may have already been provided as violations of other laws, rules, or sections of the PPA; however, these acts listed could result in separate consequences under this section of the PPA. When one of the acts listed occurs, in addition to facing discipline by the PBOP, one could also face civil and/or criminal legal proceedings under the PPA. Any person who is found to have violated this section of the PPA is guilty of a misdemeanor, and if convicted will be sentenced to one year in prison and/or a fine of up to $5,000. Each offense

thereafter will result in up to three years in prison and/or a fine of up to $15,000.

2. Acts that are considered unlawful under the PPA include:
   a. Any person to obtain or attempt to obtain a license, permit, or certificate for himself or for any other person by making or causing to be made any false representations.
   b. Any person not properly licensed as a pharmacist that engages in the practice of pharmacy. This section does not apply to pharmacy interns or other authorized personnel under the direct and immediate personal supervision of a pharmacist, as well as other individuals and establishments properly selling OTC products.

STUDY TIP: The PPA provides that this section is not to be interpreted as preventing a licensed medical practitioner from dispensing, compounding, or otherwise giving any drug to his/her own patients after diagnosis or treatment of the patient, and as long as the medication is provided to the patient by the medical practitioner. This means that in Pennsylvania, physicians and other prescribers are authorized to dispense medications to their patients.

   c. Any pharmacist that dispenses an emergency prescription refill that does not meet the requirements of the PPA. *See Chapter 4, Section II. A.5.*
   d. Any unlicensed person to operate or conduct, or to have charge of or to supervise any pharmacy. For this section, the pharmacy owner will also be found liable if this occurs.
   e. Any person who represents him/herself to be licensed under the PPA when in fact he/she is not.
   f. Any person that knowingly prevents or refuses to allow any member of the PBOP (or its agents) to enter a pharmacy or any other place that provides drugs to consumers, when the purpose to enter is to conduct a lawful inspection or other legally permitted activity.
   g. Any person whose license, permit, or certificate has been revoked, suspended, or refused renewal that fails to deliver the license, permit, or certificate to the Board upon demand.
   h. Any person to sell at auction drugs or devices in bulk or in open or unopened packages, unless the sale was approved in advance by the Board and it was done

under the personal supervision of a licensed pharmacist appointed by the Board.

i. Any individual or company to fraudulently use the title "pharmacist" or "pharmacy."

j. Any person who buys or sells any drug or device which bears, or did bear, the inscription "sample" or "not for resale" or "for investigational or experimental use only" or other similar words. An exception applies to the costs associated with the legal use of investigational or experimental drugs.

k. Any pharmacist or owner of a pharmacy advertising or promoting prices for drug and pharmaceutical service to the public which do not conform to Federal laws or regulations.

l. Any person who knowingly and willfully is involved in the forging or counterfeiting of goods.

m. Any person to obtain or attempt to obtain for him/herself or another any drug:

(1) By fraud, deceit, misrepresentation, or subterfuge;

(2) By the forgery or alteration of a prescription or any written order;

(3) By the concealment of a material fact; and/or

(4) By use of a false statement in any prescription, order, or report.

Note: This section would also apply to a person not licensed under the PPA. For example, an individual that altered a prescription to obtain the medication could be criminally charged under the PPA in addition to any other laws violated.

n. Any person to advertise the filling or refilling of prescriptions for any consumer or patient in Pennsylvania if said person is not licensed under this act or the said prescription is not filled or refilled in a pharmacy licensed by the Board.

o. One or more medical practitioners to have a proprietary or beneficial interest sufficient to permit them to exercise supervision or control over the pharmacist in his/her professional responsibilities and duties.

CHAPTER FIVE
USP Chapters and Compounding Laws and Rules

CHAPTER FIVE
USP Chapters and Compounding Laws and Rules

Special thanks to Patricia Kienle, RPh, MPA, BCSCP, FASHP,
for providing the summaries of the USP chapters.

This chapter provides an overview of the primary USP chapters dealing with pharmacy compounding. Several of the MPJE competency statements deal with compounding, and compounding questions may be asked on the MPJE. USP Chapters 795 (nonsterile), 797 (sterile), and 800 (hazardous drugs) are the chapters most frequently adopted by states regarding compounding. In addition, USP Chapter 800 is specifically mentioned in the competency statements. As discussed in Chapter 1, some states, including Pennsylvania, have adopted these chapters by reference.

I. **Introduction**
   A. Legal Recognition
      1. USP sets standards for identity, strength, quality, and purity of medications. The standards are published in the United States Pharmacopeia–National Formulary (USP-NF) compendium.
      2. USP standards are recognized in the federal Food, Drug, and Cosmetic Act (FDCA) and in various state laws and regulations. USP Chapters are considered "compendially applicable," meaning they are enforceable under federal regulations when they are numbered under 1000 and they are referenced in a General Notice, monograph, or another chapter numbered under 1000.

STUDY TIP: When standards use the terms "must" or "shall," it is a requirement. When standards use the term "should," it is a recommendation.

   B. USP Components
      1. USP General Notices provide basic information for use of the standards, such as descriptions of dosage forms, temperature requirements, and other information.
      2. USP General Chapters contain established procedures, methods, and practices. USP 795, 797, and 800 are examples of General Chapters.

3. USP Monographs contain specific information about a formulation or compound. The *USP Compounding Compendium* contains over 200 different compounding monographs.
4. Monographs are more specific than General Chapters. General Chapters are more specific than General Notices. When information conflicts, the more specific document applies.

C. Enforcement
1. USP does not enforce the standards. Enforcement is accomplished by states and by accreditation organizations that incorporate the standards into their requirements.
2. The FDCA mandates use of USP standards for compounding. When bulk drug substances (active pharmaceutical ingredients, or APIs) are used, those APIs must comply with the standards in a USP monograph (if one exists) and the applicable USP compounding standard (795 for nonsterile compounding or 797 for sterile compounding).
3. The 2013 Drug Quality and Security Act (DQSA) reaffirmed USP's authority over compounding in Section 503A. This Act distinguishes 503A entities (compounding pharmacies which supply patient-specific preparations) from 503B entities (outsourcing facilities which supply non-patient-specific preparations). Generally, 503A pharmacies are governed by state boards and follow USP compounding chapters. 503B outsourcing facilities are governed by the Food and Drug Administration (FDA) and must comply with more stringent current Good Manufacturing Practices (cGMPs).

D. Compounding
1. The FDA exempts compounding from the rigorous requirements for a new drug application, provided the compound is made by a licensed pharmacist or physician and complies with the USP Chapters on pharmacy compounding. The FDA also provides other guidance documents related to compounding.
2. States define compounding in their pharmacy rules and regulations.
3. Four General Chapters provide compounding information.
   a. USP 795 Pharmaceutical Compounding—Nonsterile Preparations
   b. USP 797 Pharmaceutical Compounding—Sterile Preparations

    c. USP 800 Hazardous Drug—Handling in Healthcare Settings

    d. USP 825 Radiopharmaceuticals—Preparation, Compounding, Dispensing, and Repackaging
    Note: USP 825 is not covered in this book.

II. USP 795 Pharmaceutical Compounding—Nonsterile Preparations
USP Chapter 795 was last revised in 2014. A proposed revision was published in 2021, but is not yet official. This information highlights the currently official (2014) version.

  A. Introduction and Scope

    1. Chapter 795 provides minimal standards for compounding nonsterile formulations (Compounded Nonsterile Preparations, CNSPs) for human and animal patients. It guides the compounder in practices to ensure CNSPs have the strength, quality, and purity intended.

    2. Chapter 795 applies to all healthcare personnel who compound CNSPs.

    3. Applicable federal and state laws and regulations concerning compounding must also be followed.

    4. If hazardous drugs are compounded, both USP 795 and USP 800 (*Hazardous Drugs—Handling in Healthcare Settings*) apply. The Occupational Safety and Health Administration (OSHA) and the National Institute for Occupational Safety and Health (NIOSH) have additional guidance concerning hazardous drugs.

  B. Categories of Compounding

    1. Simple compounding includes preparation of CNSPs according to USP monographs, use of manufacturer's information to reconstitute a commercial product, or following the complete directions in a peer-reviewed journal.

    2. Moderate compounding includes preparations requiring special calculations or procedures or mixing a CNSP for which the stability data is not known.

    3. Complex compounding includes preparing CNSPs that require special procedures or equipment.

    4. The categories of compounding do not affect the assignment of beyond-use dates (BUDs) for nonsterile compounds.

C. Responsibilities of Compounders
1. USP 795 uses the term "compounders" to mean both the person supervising compounding and personnel who compound CNSPs.
2. The compounder is responsible for preparing CNSPs of intended strength, quality, and purity.
3. Training.
   a. Compounders must be trained and able to demonstrate competence for assigned activities.
   b. The supervisor must demonstrate procedures to the compounder, who must then perform the compounding for the supervisor.
   c. All training must be documented.
   d. Compounders should document competency at least annually.

D. Facilities
1. A dedicated compounding area must be defined and limited to authorized personnel. The area must be clean, orderly, and sanitary.
2. Temperature and ventilation control must be adequate.

3. Space for orderly placement of equipment, ingredients, and other components must be available.
4. Compounding CNSPs made with hazardous drugs must also follow the requirements in USP 800 to protect the patient, compounder, and environment.
5. Compounding for sterile preparations must follow the requirements of USP 797.
6. The compounding area must have a source of potable water for washing equipment and performing hand hygiene.

7. Sinks for hand and equipment washing and other devices (e.g., dishwasher) must be accessible to the compounding area.
8. The plumbing system must be free of defects that could compromise the CNSP.
9. Appropriate waste containers must be available, and proper handling and disposal must be done.
10. Equipment
    a. Equipment must be clean, properly maintained, and intended for use for compounding.
    b. Purified water should be used for rinsing equipment and other devices (e.g., spatulas, glassware) used in compounding.

STUDY TIP: There is no requirement in the 2008 version of USP 795 to compound preparations in a powder containment hood, but many pharmacies use this device to avoid contaminating themselves or cross-contaminating CNSPs when powders or drugs that aerosolize are manipulated.

E. Hand Hygiene, Garb, and Personal Protective Equipment (PPE)
   1. Compounders' clothing must be clean and suitable for the type of compounding performed.
   2. Hand hygiene (i.e., hand washing) must be performed as detailed in the organization's policy.
   3. Garb and PPE include hair covers, face masks, gloves, gowns, and shoe covers. Additional PPE is required when compounding hazardous drugs (HDs).
F. Standard Operating Procedures (SOPs) and Other Documentation
   1. SOPs.
      a. The person in charge of compounding needs to establish and maintain adequate policies and procedures to ensure safe and reproducible CNSPs. SOPs should include details concerning facilities, equipment, personnel, receipt, storage, compounding, and other related elements.
      b. When errors or other excursions occur, policies should guide the process to identify and correct the occurrence.
   2. Safety Data Sheets (SDS).
      Safety Data Sheets (formerly called Material Safety Data Sheets, or MSDS) must be available to personnel working with bulk chemicals or other specific drugs.

3. A Master Formulation Record (MFR) must be created for each CNSP. The MFR must include:
   a. Official name, strength, and dosage form.
   b. Calculations needed.
   c. Description of all ingredients and their amounts.
   d. References for compatibility and stability.
   e. Equipment needed.
   f. Mixing instructions.
   g. Labeling information.
   h. Container to use for dispensing.
   i. Packaging and storage requirements.
   j. Description of the final CNSP.
   k. Quality control procedures and expected results.
4. A Compounding Record (CR) must be created each time a CNSP is mixed. The CR must include:
   a. Official or assigned name, strength, and dosage.
   b. MFR reference.
   c. Names and quantities of all components.
   d. Total quantity compounded.
   e. Names of personnel who compounded, performed quality control, and approved the CNSP.
   f. Date of preparation.
   g. Assigned BUD.
   h. Copy of the label.
   i. Description of the final CNSP.
   j. Results of quality control procedures.
   k. Documentation of any quality control excursions or other problems reported by the patient or caregiver.

STUDY TIP: The MFR is the recipe for the CNSP. It provides complete instructions for compounding and promotes reproducibility of the CNSP for future compounding. The CR includes the details of a specific CNSP, such as the lot number and expiration dates of each component, personnel involved in the compounding, BUD, etc.

---

5. Records must be retained for the time required for prescriptions in state regulations. For Pennsylvania this is 2 years.
G. Ingredients
   1. Ingredients (sometimes called "components") of a CNSP include:
      a. Active Pharmaceutical Ingredient (API), the ingredient that provides the pharmacological activity of the CNSP.

    b. Vehicle, such as the diluent used.

    c. Added substances, an inactive ingredient in the CNSP (sometimes called the "excipient").

2. Ingredients must be obtained from reliable sources and stored according to manufacturer's information and applicable laws and regulations. When possible, ingredients meeting standards of the United States Pharmacopeia (USP), National Formulary (NF), or Food Chemicals Codex (FCC) should be used. Ingredients should be obtained from FDA-registered facilities when possible.

3. Ingredients must be stored appropriately and cannot be stored on the floor. Ingredients that have a manufacturer's or supplier's expiration date may be used through that date as long as the container is stored to avoid decomposition of the contents. If no expiration date is provided, the compounder must assign a date that is no longer than 3 years from the date of receipt.

STUDY TIP: Notice that the BUD assigned for a component without a manufacturer's expiry must be based on the date the component was received, not the date it was opened.

---

4. Active Pharmaceutical Ingredients (APIs) are the raw powders (sometimes called "bulk substances") used for compounding. Applicable Safety Data Sheets (SDS) and other required documentation must be available for compounders.

5. APIs that are not USP or NF grade must be accompanied by a lot-specific Certificate of Analysis (COA).

6. Ingredients used for compounding CNSPs for humans must not be those that have been withdrawn from the market for safety purposes.

7. Ingredients used for compounding CNSPs for food-producing animals must not be on the federal list of components prohibited. If an ingredient is derived from a ruminant animal (e.g., bovine, caprine, ovine), the supplier must provide written information that the ingredient is in compliance with laws and regulations for the component.

8. Weighing, measuring, and mixing of ingredients must be performed and verified to be sure the CNSP contains the expected qualities.

9. When water is included in a CNSP, purified water must be used.

H. Compounding

    1. Any CNSP mixed must be evaluated for suitability and safety, including evaluation of properties of the CNSP, dosage form, appropriateness for use, and legal limitations.

    2. Compounding must be limited to one preparation at a time in a specific workspace.

    3. Assignment of beyond-use dates (BUDs).

        a. The BUD is the date beyond which a CNSP must not be used.

        b. The CNSP must maintain purity, potency/strength, quality, and expected characteristics through the BUD assigned.

STUDY TIP: Expiration dates are provided by manufacturers for their products. BUDs are established by compounders for their preparations.

---

        c. For CNSPs that do not have stability information for the specific formulation (including drug, diluent, container, and closure), the compounder must limit the BUDs assigned to the following:

Type of Formulation	Maximum BUD
Water-containing oral formulation	14 days (*refrigerated*)
Water-containing topical/dermal and mucosal liquid and semi-solid formulations	30 days
Nonaqueous formulations	6 months

        d. BUDs may be extended beyond the default dates above if stability studies of the formulation are conducted with appropriate results, or if a USP monograph is followed exactly and contains a longer BUD.

        e. The BUD cannot be longer than the expiration date of any of its components.

    4. Labeling.

        a. CNSPs must be labeled as detailed in the Master Formulation Record and include all elements required by laws and regulations.

        b. CNSP labels should include: "This is a compounded preparation."

        c. Labels of CNSPs for food-producing animals must include the withdrawal time (WDT) provided by the veterinarian. The WDT indicates the length of time that animal tissue of food-producing animals cannot be used for human food supply.

I. Dispensing

    1. All applicable laws and regulations must be followed when dispensing CNSPs.

    2. Packaging must meet USP requirements.

    3. Appropriate consultation should be provided to the patient or caregiver.

J. Quality control and final check of CNSPs

    1. The compounder must compare the elements of the CNSP (e.g., weight, clarity, color, odor, consistency, pH, other testing as required) to the Master Formulation Record.

    2. The CNSP must be packaged as detained in the Master Formulation Record.

    3. A method to recall CNSPs must be developed in case that action is necessary.

III. USP 797 Pharmaceutical Compounding—Sterile Preparations

USP Chapter 797 was last revised in 2008. A proposed revision was published in 2021, but is not yet official. This information highlights the currently official (2008) version.

A. Introduction and Scope

    1. Chapter 797 provides standards to prevent harm that could occur from microbial, chemical, or physical contamination; incorrect strength; or inappropriate quality of compounded sterile preparations (CSPs) for human and animal patients.

    2. Chapter 797 applies to all healthcare personnel who compound CNSPs and applies in all healthcare settings.

    3. CSPs include drugs and biologics such as injections, infusions, irrigations for wounds and body cavities, ophthalmics (including drops), tissue implants, baths and soaks for organs and tissues, aqueous bronchial and nasal inhalations, and other preparations intended to be sterile.

    4. Applicable state and federal laws and regulations concerning compounding must also be followed.

    5. If hazardous drugs are compounded, both USP 797 and USP 800 (*Hazardous Drugs—Handling in Healthcare Settings*) apply. The Occupational Safety and Health Administration (OSHA) and the National Institute for Occupational Safety and Health (NIOSH) have additional guidance concerning hazardous drugs.

6. USP 797 has sections concerning the special requirements for preparation of allergen extracts and radio-
pharmaceuticals. The radiopharmaceutical information is
now supplemented by a new USP Chapter: USP 825 *Radio-
pharmaceuticals—Preparation, Compounding, Dispensing,
and Repackaging.*

B. Categories of CSPs
1. Immediate Use are those mixed outside of the facilities
described in the chapter when the urgency does not permit mixing in a cleanroom suite or segregated compounding
area (SCA). Immediate Use preparations are limited to simple transfer of not more than 3 sterile manufactured ingredients and not more than 2 entries into any one container.
2. Low Risk CSPs are those mixed in a USP 797–compliant area
as a single dose for one patient.
3. Medium Risk CSPs are those mixed in a USP 797–compliant
area as a batch for multiple patients or for one patient on
multiple occasions, or more complex mixtures such as Total
Parenteral Nutrition (TPN) solutions.
4. High Risk CSPs are those mixed in a USP 797–compliant
cleanroom suite with a nonsterile starting ingredient, or any
risk level if mixed without complete garb as required.
5. The risk levels are key elements in determining the beyond-
use dates (BUDs) for sterile compounds.

STUDY TIP: Examples of types of risk levels include:
- Low—reconstituting a vial of cefazolin and placing it in a piggyback IV bag.
- Medium—making a batch of 10 antibiotic syringes.
- High—mixing an alum irrigation from an active pharmaceutical
  ingredient (API).

C. Responsibilities of Compounders
1. The compounder is responsible for preparing CSPs that are
accurately mixed, within 10% of labeled strength/potency
(unless otherwise listed), and prepared with appropriate
technique in proper facilities.
2. Training
   a. Compounders must be trained and able to demonstrate
   competence for assigned activities.
   b. Initial training includes theoretical principles, practical skills including aseptic work practices, observation

of expert compounders, return demonstrations, and successful completion of written competences, hand hygiene and garbing, a gloved fingertip test without any contamination, and media fill tests.

c. Requalifying training includes successful completion of written tests, media fill tests, and requalifying gloved fingertip tests. The media fill tests and requalifying glove fingertip tests must be done at least every 6 months if high-risk CSPs are mixed, or at least every 12 months if only low- and medium-risk CSPs are mixed.

d. Media fill tests must mimic the most complex CSP mixed. A successful media fill test is one that shows no growth or cloudiness over the time period of the test.

e. Gloved fingertip tests are done at initial training (to check for the ability to aseptically garb) and as a requalifying test at the same frequency as required for media fill tests.

STUDY TIP: Action Levels—the maximum number of microbial colony forming units (CFUs) allowed—are listed in USP 797 for the gloved fingertip test. Initially, the compounder needs to complete 3 sets (6 plates) with no growth to demonstrate the ability to repeatedly garb without contamination themselves. For requalification, the same test is done, but it is done following a media fill after other compounding. Only 1 set (2 plates) is required, and the number of CFUs cannot exceed 3 on both plates.

---

f. All training must be documented.

D. Facilities

1. The sterile compounding area must be properly designed with cleanable surfaces and should have a temperature under 20°C. No humidity requirement is listed in the 2008 version of USP 795, but the relative humidity should be under 60%. Some states have specific requirements.

2. Primary Engineering Controls

a. Primary Engineering Controls (PECs, informally called *hoods*) are the devices in which CSPs are mixed.

b. Laminar air flow workbenches (LAFWs) and biological safety cabinets (BSCs) are examples of traditional types of PECs.

c. Compounding aseptic isolators (CAIs) and compounding aseptic containment isolators (CACIs) are examples of compounding isolators.

d. PECs must meet specific criteria, including maintenance of an ISO 5 classification, have unidirectional air flow, and meet other requirements listed in USP 797.

STUDY TIP: ISO class is determined by the number of particles larger than 0.5 microns in a volume of air. The smaller the ISO number, the cleaner the air. PECs must be ISO 5 or cleaner. Anterooms that open into a negative pressure room and buffer rooms must be ISO 7 or cleaner. Anterooms that open only into positive pressure buffer rooms must be ISO 8 or cleaner.

---

3. Secondary Engineering Controls

a. Secondary Engineering Controls (SECs, informally called the IV room or IV lab) are the rooms in which the PEC is placed.

b. USP 797 details specific requirements including ISO classification, pressurization, air flow, and other characteristics.

c. There are two types of SECs:

(1) A cleanroom suite, consisting of a positive pressure anteroom and at least one buffer room. The anteroom must be positive pressure and must be at least ISO 7 if it opens into any negative pressure buffer room or at least ISO 8 if it opens only into positive pressure buffer rooms. The buffer room must be at least ISO 7.

(2) A segregated compounding area (SCA), which is an area designated for use for sterile compounding. It does not have to be a separate room, but that is preferred. A more complex containment segregated compounding area (C-SCA) is used for compounding hazardous drugs. *See Section IV. on USP 800 below for details.*

SEC	Minimum ISO Classification
Anteroom that opens only into positive pressure buffer room(s)	ISO 8
Anteroom that opens into one or more negative pressure room(s)	ISO 7
Positive pressure buffer room	ISO 7
Negative pressure buffer room	ISO 7
Segregated Compounding Area	Not required to be ISO-classified
Containment Segregated Compounding Area	Not required to be ISO-classified

4. Pressure gradients between rooms in a sterile compounding suite minimize the possibility of microbial contamination.
   a. The buffer room (where the hood is placed) must be 0.020" more positive than the anteroom.
   b. The anteroom must be 0.020" more positive than the general area it opens into.
   c. There is no pressure gradient requirement for SCAs.
   d. There is a negative pressure requirement for hazardous drug ("chemo") buffer rooms and C-SCAs. *See Section IV. on USP 800 below for details.*
5. Current (2008) USP 797 allows a clean room that is a single room with an ante area and a buffer area. A line dividing the two areas must be used to demonstrate air flow of 40 feet per minute from the buffer to ante area. This design is not recommended and is unlikely to be allowed in the future.
6. Other devices and equipment.
   a. The cleanroom suite or SCA must be designed to promote proper cleaning. Sinks, counters, pass-throughs, refrigerators, and other equipment and devices must be suitable for use in the IV room, properly placed, and cleaned.
   b. Devices specifically designed for use in the PEC, such as automated compounding devices (ACDs) and repeater pumps, must be used according to manufacturer's instructions and only by compounders who have been assessed for competence.
7. Certification—PECs and SECs must be certified every 6 months by a qualified certification technician.

E. Hand Hygiene, Garb, and Personal Protective Equipment (PPE)
   1. Hand hygiene (i.e., hand washing) must be performed as detailed in the organization's policy. Hands and forearms must be washed with soap and water up to elbows for 30 seconds.
   2. Garb and PPE includes hair covers, face masks, gloves, gowns, and shoe covers. Additional PPE is required when compounding hazardous drugs (HDs).

3. There is a specific order in which to don garb and perform hand hygiene:
   a. Don head and hair covers, masks, and shoe covers upon entry to the anteroom or SCA.
   b. In an anteroom, step over into the clean side of the room.
   c. Perform hand hygiene.
   d. Don gown.
   e. Apply alcohol-based hand rub to hands and allow to dry.
   f. Don sterile gloves.

F. Standard Operating Procedures (SOPs) and Other Documentation
   1. Standard Operating Procedures (SOPs).
      a. The person in charge of compounding needs to establish and maintain adequate policies and procedures to ensure safe and reproducible CNSPs. SOPs should include details concerning facilities, equipment, personnel, receipt, storage, compounding, and other related elements.
      b. When errors or other excursions occur, policies should guide the process to identify and correct the occurrence.
   2. Master Formulation Records and Compounding Records are not required in the 2008 version of USP 797, but similar records are necessary. Appropriate records should be developed and maintained, such as logs for batches of CSPs made.

G. Compounding Technique
   1. Aseptic technique is a core practice that must be mastered.
   2. Maintaining sterility of critical sites is essential. Critical sites are areas such as vial septa, ports, needle hubs, and other surfaces at highest risk of exposure to contamination.

H. Components
   1. Ingredients must be obtained from reliable sources and stored according to manufacturer's information and applicable laws and regulations. When possible, ingredients meeting standards of the United States Pharmacopeia (USP), National Formulary (NF), or Food Chemicals Codex (FCC) should be used. Ingredients should be obtained from FDA-registered facilities when possible.

2. Ingredients must be stored appropriately and cannot be stored on the floor. Ingredients that have a manufacturer's or supplier's expiration date may be used through that date as long as the container is stored to avoid decomposition of the contents. If no expiration date is provided, the compounder must assign a date that is no longer than one year from the date of receipt, unless testing proves it has retained the purity and quality required.

3. Active Pharmaceutical Ingredients (APIs) are the raw powders (sometimes called "bulk substances") used for compounding. Applicable Safety Data Sheets (SDS) and other required documentation must be available for compounders.

4. APIs that are not USP or NF grade must be accompanied by a lot-specific Certificate of Analysis (COA).

5. Ingredients used for compounding CSPs for humans must not be those that have been withdrawn from the market for safety purposes.

I. Compounding process

1. Most CSPs are mixed using only conventionally manufactured sterile components. The goal for sterile-to-sterile compounding is to maintain sterility.

2. High-risk CSPs are mixed using nonsterile starting ingredients. The goal for nonsterile-to-sterile compounding is to achieve sterility. Sterilization of the final CSP is achieved using terminal sterilization (such as in an autoclave using steam under pressure) or by filtration. Both methods require quality control measures to ensure they have performed as intended.

   a. Autoclaving is monitored using biological indicators.

   b. Filtration is checked by performing a bubble point test of the used filter to ensure its integrity.

STUDY TIP: Terminal sterilization is described in USP 797 as by use of an autoclave (steam under pressure) or dry heat. Filtration is not terminal sterilization.

---

3. High-risk CSPs (except those for inhalation or ophthalmic administration) that are made in groups of more than 25 units must also pass a bacterial endotoxin (pyrogen) test.

4. Components used for preparation of CSPs have limited in-use times:

Type of component	Allowable in-use time when opened in and maintained in ISO 5	Allowable in-use time when opened outside of or removed from ISO 5
Ampule	Use and discard remainder	Use and discard remainder
Single-dose vial	Up to 6 hours	Up to 1 hour
Multiple-dose vial	Up to 28 days (unless manufacturer's instructions differ)	Up to 28 days (unless manufacturer's instructions differ)

5. Assignment of beyond-use dates (BUDs).
   a. The BUD is the date beyond which a CSP must not be used.

STUDY TIP: Expiration dates are provided by manufacturers for their products. BUDs are established by compounders for their preparations.

   b. BUDs for CSPs that do not have stability information for the specific formulation (including drug, diluent, container, and closure) must limit the BUDs assigned to the following:

Category	Stored at controlled room temperature	Stored under refrigeration	Stored frozen
Immediate Use	1 hour	Not applicable	Not applicable
Low Risk made in an SCA	12 hours	12 hours	Not applicable
Low Risk	48 hours	14 days	45 days
Medium Risk	30 hours	9 days	45 days
High Risk	24 hours	3 days	45 days

STUDY TIP: You should be familiar with different BUDs based on storage conditions and risk levels.

   c. BUDs may be extended beyond the default dates above if stability studies of the formulation are conducted with appropriate results or if a USP monograph is followed exactly and contains a longer BUD.
   d. The BUD cannot be longer than the expiration date of any of its components.
6. Labeling
   Labels of CSPs must include the drug name and strength/concentration, total volume, BUD, route of administration,

and storage conditions. Other information to support safe use, organizational policy, and state laws and regulations must be included as appropriate.

J. Dispensing the Final Preparation

   1. The compounder must check the final CSP prior to dispensing. Identification of the individual who checked the final CSP must be documented.

   2. Many CSPs require storage at refrigerator temperature if not immediately dispensed. Those CSPs that will be shipped to a location other than where they are compounded (e.g., to a patient's home) must have appropriate temperature control.

K. Cleaning the Compounding Areas

   1. Solutions used must be appropriate for use in a clean-room and (if necessary) properly diluted. Many solutions have a "dwell time," which is the time the solution needs to be wet and in contact with the surface in order to achieve its intended result (e.g., decontamination, cleaning, disinfection).

   2. Cleaning PECs and SECs is done with a detergent. After cleaning, the PEC needs to have sterile 70% isopropyl alcohol applied to the surface of the PEC.

   3. The PEC surface must be cleaned at the beginning of each shift, before each batch, every 30 minutes during compounding, after spills, and when surface contamination is known or suspected.

   4. Floors, counters, and other easily cleanable surfaces (e.g., refrigerator handles, pass-through chambers) must be cleaned daily.

   5. Storage shelving, walls, and ceilings must be cleaned at least monthly.

   6. Only compounding personnel can clean the PECs, but some organizations allow others with documented competency to clean floors, walls, and ceilings.

L. Environmental Monitoring

   1. Environmental monitoring consists of non-viable (e.g., temperature, pressure gradients, air flow) and viable (microbial contamination) elements.

   2. Some non-viable parameters must be monitored daily by compounding personnel:

   a. Temperature of the compounding areas, which should be 20°C or lower to minimize the risk of microbial contamination and for the comfort of the garbed compounder. If drugs are stored in the compounding area, the required temperature range for the drugs must be maintained.

b. Pressure gradients between rooms. USP 797 requires minimum pressure gradients between rooms. Positive pressure rooms assist in preventing contamination entering the room, so they are used for anterooms and nonhazardous buffer rooms. Negative pressure rooms assist in containing hazards, so are used for hazardous ("chemo") buffer rooms.

Between	Minimum pressure gradient required
Nonhazardous buffer room to anteroom	Buffer room must be at least 0.020" more positive than the anteroom
Hazardous buffer room to anteroom	Buffer room must be between 0.010 and 0.030" negative to anteroom
Anteroom to adjacent general area	Anteroom must be at least 0.020" more positive than general area
Segregated Compounding Area	No requirement
Containment Segregated Compounding Area to adjacent general area	C-SCA must be between 0.010 to 0.030" negative to adjacent area

STUDY TIP: Be sure to know the minimum pressure gradients required between areas.

c. Combined ante/buffer rooms must have a displacement air flow of at least 40 feet per minute over the line of demarcation from the buffer area to the ante area.

3. Certification.
Certification involves a qualified technician checking and ensuring that non-viable parameters listed in USP 797 (e.g., particle counts, air flow, proper pressurization, and other elements) are within manufacturer's and industry specifications. PECs must be certified every six months and after servicing. SECs must be certified every six months or when changes are made in the room that could affect the air flow.

4. Viable monitoring.
a. The facilities in which low-, medium-, and high-risk CSPs are made must be monitored to ensure microbial

(bacterial and fungal) contaminants are not present to a degree that could harm patients.

b. Viable monitoring is accomplished with electronic air sampling and surface sampling.

c. Electronic air sampling must be checked at least every 6 months. Surface sampling must be checked periodically. Most organizations have their certifiers perform this sampling. Many organizations supplement these semiannual checks with additional sampling. Facilities that mix only low- and medium-risk-level CSPs must test for bacteria; facilities mixing high-risk-level CSPs must test for bacteria and fungus. However, most organizations test for both bacteria and fungus, even if they mix only low- and medium-risk CSPs.

d. Action Levels based on the maximum number of CFUs allowed are listed in USP 797. If the action levels are exceeded or if trends are noted, the compounder needs to consult with a trained microbiologist to develop a remedial plan. Organisms exceeding the action level should be identified at least to the genus level. Highly pathogenic organisms (e.g., gram-negative rods, coagulase positive staphylococcus, molds, and yeasts) must be immediately remedied even if they do not exceed the action level.

ACTION LEVELS IN NUMBER OF COLONY FORMING UNITS (CFUS)

ISO Classification	Air Sample (per 1,000 liters of air)	Surface Sample (per plate)
ISO 5 (PECs)	> 1	> 3
ISO 7 (buffer rooms and anteroom opening into a negative pressure room)	> 10	> 5
ISO 8 (anteroom opening only into positive pressure buffer rooms)	> 100	> 100

M. Quality Control
1. A policy needs to be established to describe the elements of control that support safe sterile compounding.
2. The elements should be specific and measurable and identify the follow-up that would occur if excursions beyond stated limits occur.

IV. USP 800 Hazardous Drugs—Compounding in Healthcare Settings

USP Chapter 800 became official on December 1, 2019. Generally, USP chapters numbered under 1000 are considered "compendially applicable," meaning they are enforceable under federal regulations. In this unusual situation, 800 is not yet compendially applicable because its enforceability is tied to the revisions of USP 795 or USP 797, which refer to USP 800. Some states and accreditation organizations expect compliance now; others, including the PBOP, will wait for the revisions of 795 and 797 to become official. At the time this book was published, the PBOP was enforcing USP 795 and USP 797 as currently written and delaying the enforcement of USP 800 until the 795 and 797 revisions were resolved.

A. Introduction and Scope
1. Chapter 800 details practice and quality standards for handling hazardous drugs (HDs) in various healthcare settings. The chapter discusses the handling of HDs from receipt to storage, compounding, dispensing, administration, and disposal of both nonsterile and sterile preparations. Included in the chapter is information on proper engineering controls and quality standards, personnel training, labeling, packaging, and transport and disposal of HDs, along with measures for spill control, documentation of all aspects of the handling of HDs, and medical surveillance.
2. Chapter 800 applies to all healthcare personnel and all entities who handle hazardous drugs. These personnel and entities include, but are not limited to, pharmacists, pharmacy technicians, pharmacies, physicians, nurses, hospital physician assistants, home healthcare workers, physician practice facilities, veterinarians, veterinary technicians, and veterinary hospitals and facilities. Entities that handle HDs must incorporate Chapter 800 standards into occupational safety standards.
3. The Occupational Safety and Health Administration (OSHA) includes hazardous drugs in their hazardous materials requirements, but does not include details of specific agents. Some states have additional state OSHA requirements.

B. List of Hazardous Drugs
1. The National Institute of Occupational Safety and Health (NIOSH) maintains a list of hazardous drugs (HDs) used in healthcare. This list is updated approximately every 2 years.

Chapter 800 requires any entity that stores, compounds, prepares, transports, or administers hazardous drugs to maintain a list of HDs used in the entity and to review the list at least every 12 months and update whenever a new agent or dosage form is used. Newly marketed HDs or dosage forms should be reviewed against the entity's list.

2. The NIOSH list comprises drugs that are hazardous to healthcare workers. These are drugs that are carcinogens, genotoxins, teratogens, reproductive toxins, or cause organ toxicity at low doses. This is a different situation than hazardous materials defined by the Environmental Protection Agency (EPA), which are hazardous to the environment. A few hazardous drugs are listed on both lists.

3. Some dosage forms of drugs defined as hazardous drugs may not pose a substantial risk of direct occupational exposure to healthcare workers. However, particulate matter from tablets, capsules, and/or packaging materials could present an exposure risk if it contacts skin or mucous membranes. Facilities using hazardous drugs must perform an assessment of risk at least annually to determine if new or alternate containment strategies need to be employed to mitigate risks for exposure from HDs.

4. Unintentional exposures to hazardous drugs have been documented. These include transdermal and transmucosal absorption, injection, and ingestion. Containers of HDs have been shown to be contaminated upon arrival to their intended destination. Accidental exposure is also possible for individuals handling body fluids; deactivating, decontaminating, or disinfecting areas contaminated with HDs; and/or contacting HD residue on drug containers, work surfaces, etc.

C. Responsibilities of Personnel Handling Hazardous Drugs
1. The chapter requires that each entity have a designated person to be responsible for developing and implementing HD handling procedures. This individual must be properly trained and qualified to oversee entity compliance with the chapter and applicable state and federal laws and regulations and to ensure competency of all individuals who may come into contact with HDs.

STUDY TIP: USP does not require the Designated Person to be a pharmacist, but some states may require that. The Designated Person does not need to be a manager, and that person may have responsibility for more than one location.

2. All persons involved in the handling of HDs must have a fundamental understanding of practices and precautions and of the evaluation of procedures to ensure the safety and quality of the final HD product or preparation to minimize the risk of harm to the intended patient.

D. Facilities and Engineering Controls
1. At each stage of the handling of HDs there must be conditions and policies in place to promote safety for patients, workers, and the environment.
2. Signs must be placed at entrances to HD handling areas. Access to these areas of a facility should be limited only to properly trained and authorized personnel.
3. The chapter requires that there be designated areas for receiving and unpacking HDs, for storing HDs, and for compounding of nonsterile and sterile preparations.
4. Certain areas must have a negative pressure gradient with respect to surrounding areas of the facilities to reduce the risk of contaminating areas where non-HD-authorized individuals work. These negative pressure areas should have an

uninterrupted power source in the event of a loss of power to the facility.

E. Receipt of HDs

   1. According to Chapter 800, all HDs and all hazardous drug active pharmaceutical ingredients (HD-APIs) must be removed from shipping containers in an area that is negative pressure or neutral pressure relative to the surrounding areas. General receiving areas are acceptable as long as they are not positive pressure areas.

   2. In addition, shipping cartons containing HDs and/or HD-APIs must not be opened in sterile compounding or positive pressure areas.

F. Storage of HDs

   1. HDs must be stored in areas that can prevent or contain spillage or breakage of a container if it falls. However, HDs must not be stored on the floor.

   2. Antineoplastic HDs in NIOSH Table 1 that will be compounded to make the final preparation, and Active Pharmaceutical Ingredient (API) of any NIOSH HDs, must be stored in an area away from non-HDs to prevent contamination or personnel exposure.

   3. The room for storage of NIOSH Table 1 antineoplastic HDs that will be compounded and HD-APIs must be vented to the exterior of the facility and must have at least 12 air changes per hour (ACPH).

   4. Final dosage forms of NIOSH Table 1 HDs and other HDs may be stored with non-HD drug inventory if permitted by entity policy in the Assessment of Risk.

G. Compounding with HDs

   1. To help minimize the risk of exposure in a pharmacy compounding HDs, detailed standard operating procedures (SOPs) and training requirements must be developed. Workers must wear personal protective equipment (PPE) designed to be resistant to hazardous drugs. Goggles and face shields should be worn if splashing is possible, and respiratory protection should be worn if the HD is volatile or if particulate matter can become airborne.

   2. Containment engineering controls to protect a preparation from microbial (if final preparation is to be sterile) and cross-contamination are required throughout the compounding procedures.

3. Containment engineering controls are divided into three types:
   a. Containment Primary Engineering Control (C-PEC);
   b. Containment Secondary Engineering Control (C-SEC); and
   c. Containment Supplemental Engineering Controls.
4. A C-PEC is a ventilated device designed to minimize the risk of exposure to the compounder and to the environment when HDs are handled directly. Containment Ventilated Enclosures (CVEs, often called powder containment hoods) are devices used only for nonsterile preparations. Biological Safety Cabinets (BSCs) and Compounding Aseptic Containment Isolators (CACIs) are used for sterile preparations and must maintain ISO 5 air cleanliness and have unidirectional air flow. The C-PEC must be operated continuously if used for sterile compounding or if it supplies some or all of the negative pressure for the room.

5. A C-SEC is the room in which the C-PEC is located. It can be a compounding suite (containing an anteroom and buffer room) or a containment segregated compounding area.
6. C-SECs must be used for compounding both nonsterile and sterile preparations and must:
   a. Be a room with fixed walls that is separate from non-hazardous storage or compounding;
   b. Have a negative pressure gradient of 0.010–0.030″ with respect to adjacent areas;
   c. Have appropriate air exchange (ACPH); and
   d. Be vented to the exterior of the facility.

7. Containment supplemental engineering controls, such as closed system drug-transfer devices (CSTDs), provide

additional protection from exposure of the compounder to one or more HDs. CSTDs must be used for administration of Table 1 NIOSH antineoplastics and should be used for compounding.

8. An eyewash station and other applicable emergency safety equipment (e.g., safety showers, fire blankets, etc.) meeting applicable laws and regulations must be readily available, and a sink must be available for hand washing. However, all water sources and drains must be located outside the buffer room and at least one meter from the C-PEC or entrance to any negative pressure room.

9. For entities where compounding of both sterile and nonsterile HDs is performed, the C-PECs must be located in separate rooms, unless the C-PECs used for nonsterile compounding can effectively maintain ISO 7 air quality in the room. If the C-PECs for nonsterile and sterile compounding are located in the same room, they must be placed at least 1 meter apart. If the C-PECs are in the same room, any nonsterile compounding that generates particulate matter may not be performed when sterile compounding is being performed.

10. A professional certifier must assess the primary and secondary engineering controls every 6 months. The C-PECs and C-SECs must meet the criteria listed in USP 797 (for facilities used for compounding sterile HDs) and USP 800 (for all facilities that compound HDs).

H. Nonsterile Compounding with HDs

1. In addition to following the regulations set forth in this chapter, entities involved in compounding nonsterile preparation, regardless of whether the compounding involves HDs or not, must also comply with the requirements of USP Chapter 795, Pharmaceutical Compounding—Nonsterile Preparations.

2. A C-PEC may not be required if the entity compounds only nonsterile, non-HD drugs, or if the entity is not manipulating HDs in any form except handling the final dosage forms (e.g., counting or repackaging tablets or capsules). This must be detailed in the Assessment of Risk.

3. C-PECs used only for nonsterile HD compounding are negative pressure devices but are not required to be ISO classified nor have unidirectional air flow.
Requirements for C-PECs and C-SECs for compounding nonsterile HDs are summarized in the following table:

ENGINEERING CONTROLS FOR NON-STERILE HD COMPOUNDING

C-PEC	C-SEC
Externally vented (preferred) or redundant-HEPA filtered with HEPA filters in series	Room separate from nonhazardous activities
	Negative pressure (0.010–0.030 inch water column) relative to adjacent areas
	Externally vented
	12 ACPH

I. Sterile Compounding with HDs
   1. In addition to following the regulations set forth in this chapter, entities involved in compounding sterile preparation, regardless of whether the compounding involves HDs or not, must also comply with the requirements of USP Chapter 797, Pharmaceutical Compounding—Sterile Preparations.
   2. All C-PECs used for the purpose of compounding sterile hazardous drugs must be vented to the outside.
   3. As is the case with PECs used in the compounding of sterile non-HD preparations, C-PECs must maintain an ISO Class 5 or better air quality.
   4. Laminar air flow workbenches or Compounding Aseptic Isolators (CAIs) are not acceptable for compounding antineoplastic HDs because they are positive pressure devices. Requirements for C-PECs and C-SECs for compounding sterile HDs are summarized in the following table:

ENGINEERING CONTROLS FOR STERILE HD COMPOUNDING

C-SEC Configuration	C-PEC Requirements	C-SEC Requirements
ISO Class 7 buffer room with ISO Class 7 anteroom	• Vented Externally • Examples: Class II BSC or CACI	• Room separate from non-hazardous activities • Vented Externally • 30 ACPH • Positive pressure anteroom • Negative pressure as described previously in buffer room
Unclassified C-SCA	• Vented Externally • Examples: Class II BSC or CACI	• Room separate from non-hazardous activities • Vented Externally • 12 ACPH • Negative pressure as described previously

J. Documentation and Standard Operating Procedures (SOPs)
1. Any entity handling HDs must maintain SOPs for safe handling of HDs at all stages and locations where HDs are found in the facility.
2. These SOPs are to be reviewed at least annually and should include a hazard communication program, occupational safety program, designation of HD areas, and items discussed above.

K. Receiving, Labeling, Packaging, Transport, and Disposal
1. A facility must establish SOPs for the receiving, labeling, packaging, transport, and disposal of HDs.
2. Transport of HDs must be labeled, stored, and handled in accordance with applicable federal, state, and local regulations.
3. HDs must be transported in containers that minimize the risk of breakage and leakage.

L. Personnel Training
All personnel who handle HDs must be properly trained based on job function. The training must be documented.

M. Personal Protective Equipment
1. NIOSH documents provide guidance on personal protective equipment (PPE) such as not reusing disposable PPE and decontaminating reusable PPE.
2. Chapter 800 requires gowns, head and hair covers, shoe covers, and two pairs of powderless chemotherapy gloves when compounding either nonsterile or sterile antineoplastic agents. Two pairs of chemotherapy gloves and gowns resistant to permeability by HDs are also required when administering injectable antineoplastic HDs. One pair of chemo gloves must be worn when receiving NIOSH Table 1 antineoplastic HDs.
3. For other activities, the facility's SOPs must describe appropriate PPE to be worn. SOPs must be based on risk of exposure and activities.
4. At all stages of the handling of HDs, from receiving to waste disposal, PPE must be worn.
5. Chemotherapy gloves must meet the American Society of Testing Materials (ASTM) standard D6978 and should be worn when handling any HD. Chapter 800 states that chemotherapy gloves should be changed every 30 minutes unless the manufacturer recommends different intervals.

6. Chapter 800 states that gowns must close in the back, be disposable, and resist permeability of HDs. Gowns must be changed per the manufacturer's information for permeation of the gown. If there is no information from the manufacturer, then Chapter 800 states gowns are to be changed every 2–3 hours or immediately after a splash or spill. Personnel are not to wear in other areas of a facility the same gown that was worn in HD handling areas.

7. A second pair of shoe covers must be donned before entering the C-SEC and must be removed before leaving the HD handling areas and entering other areas of the facility.

8. Appropriate face and eye protection are to be worn when there is a risk of spills or splashes of HDs. Safety eyeglasses with side shields do not provide adequate protection.

9. When unpacking HDs not contained in plastic, personnel should wear elastomeric half-face masks which have been fit-tested with a P100 filter and a multi-gas cartridge.

10. All worn PPE should be considered contaminated and placed in an appropriate waste container to be disposed of properly. PPE used in compounding HDs should be discarded in proper containers before leaving the C-SEC.

N. Cleaning
   1. The cleaning process for hazardous drugs must start with deactivating the drug (when possible) and decontaminating the surfaces that the HDs have touched.
   2. After decontamination, the surfaces must be cleaned then disinfected.

STUDY TIP: Few HDs have specific information concerning how to deactivate them, so decontaminating the surfaces touched in the C-PEC and C-SEC is crucial. Decontamination is done with a properly diluted oxidizer or other agent intended to eliminate HDs. Cleaning is done with a properly diluted detergent. Disinfection is done with isopropyl alcohol, which must be sterile for use in C-PECs used for sterile compounding.

O. Spill Control
   Facility policies must include the steps to take when a spill occurs.

P. Medical Surveillance
   1. As part of a comprehensive exposure control program, medical surveillance complements all other attempts by

Chapter 800 to minimize risks to healthcare workers. Medical surveillance is recommended but not required by USP 800.

2. Elements of an appropriate medical surveillance program must be consistent with an entity's policies, and medical records should be consistent with regulations set forth by the Occupational Safety and Health Administration (OSHA).

3. Chapter 800 outlines elements of a medical surveillance plan that should be included for all healthcare workers who may come into contact with hazardous drugs. The chapter also describes elements that should be included in a follow-up plan should HD exposure-related health changes occur. Again, the elements in the recommended medical surveillance and follow-up plans are not exhaustive, but they provide a good basis for the development of an appropriate program. Once again, however, any medical surveillance plan should follow entity policies.

Q. Environmental Quality and Control

1. While there are no currently accepted limits for HD surface contamination, Chapter 800 states that surface wipe sampling for HDs should be performed routinely to ensure that cleaning procedures are effective in removing remaining HD residues after handling or compounding.

2. Surface wipe sampling should include, but not necessarily be limited to, the inside surface of the C-PEC and any equipment contained in it, pass-through chambers, staging surfaces, areas adjacent to the C-PEC, areas immediately outside the buffer room or C-SEC, and patient administration areas.

3. The chapter continues by saying that if any measurable HD residue is found, the designated person should consider taking actions such as reevaluating work practices, retraining personnel, etc.

V. Pennsylvania Rules on Compounding

A. The compounding of sterile and nonsterile preparations by 503A pharmacies is to comply with the FDCA/FDA requirements and the current versions of the USP chapters governing compounding. *See PBOP 49 Pa. Code § 27.601*

1. The FDA has issued various guidance documents for 503A compounding pharmacies that are beyond the scope of this book. Detailed information can be found on the FDA

website, but a few details are provided in this section. A few specifics are provided below.

    a. 503A pharmacies are exempt from registering with the FDA, meeting cGMPs, and other FDA requirements that 503B facilities and manufacturers have to comply with. To remain exempt from these FDA requirements, 503A pharmacies are to compound patient-specific prescriptions ("office use" compounding is prohibited) and are only permitted to use FDA-approved bulk substances. Additionally, the FDA and PBOP also provide that 503A pharmacies cannot compound regularly or inordinate amounts of products that are essential copies of commercially available products or drugs that have been removed from the market after being determined unsafe or ineffective. *See PBOP 49 Pa. Code § 27.602*

    b. The FDA does allow 503A pharmacies to participate in anticipatory compounding of limited quantities based on the history of past orders (see FDA guidance for additional clarification for determining quantity limitations).

    c. The FDA has further clarified and defined through guidance the terms inordinate amounts and essential copies of commercially available products. An example includes the FDA providing that the definition of an essential copy does not include the pharmacy compounding a product where there is a change from the commercial product made for an identified individual patient that produces a significant difference for the patient.

  2. The four general USP Chapters that provide compounding information include USP 795, USP 797, USP 800, and USP 825.

B. Pennsylvania has compounding rules for pharmacists and their responsibilities, including label information and required recordkeeping. *See 49 Pa. Code §§ 27.603–27.605*

Pharmacist responsibilities regarding compounded products include:

  1. Inspection and approval or rejection of all components, bulk substances, containers, and labels.

  2. Preparation and review of all compounding records to assure that errors have not occurred in the compounding process.

  3. Proper maintenance, cleanliness, and use of all facilities and equipment used in compounding practice.

4. Conducting investigations when errors occur and keeping a record of the investigation, conclusion, and corrective actions taken.
5. Labeling the compounded product for compliance with USP and PBOP requirements. *See 49 Pa. Code § 27.18(d) for PBOP labeling requirements.*
6. Retaining required compounding records and making available to the PBOP and authorized authorities for 2 years from the date of the record.

CHAPTER SIX
Self-Assessment Questions

CHAPTER SIX
Self-Assessment Questions

Important: These questions should help you determine your level of understanding of the material in this book and your general knowledge of the most important federal and state laws and rules likely to appear on the MPJE. No representation is made that these questions are similar to questions on the actual MPJE.

1. Pharmacist Bill orders and receives a bottle of generic glipizide from his supplier. Bill notices the label of the bottle is crooked and some of the lettering on the label appears to have different fonts in the same word. Bill calls the supplier to verify the transaction data and learns that the lot number on the bottle is not a valid lot number for that brand of glipizide. What is Bill required to do? **Select all that apply.**
   a. Notify FDA and all trading partners of this illegitimate product.
   b. Take steps to work with the manufacturer to prevent the illegitimate product from reaching patients.
   c. Order a Class I recall of the drug.
   d. Notify DEA.

2. Which of the following is not required on the label of an OTC product?
   a. Adequate directions for safe and effective use
   b. Name and address of the manufacturer, packager, or distributor
   c. Inactive ingredients
   d. Patient Package Insert

3. Fiorinal® is classified as
   a. A listed chemical
   b. A Schedule III controlled substance
   c. A Schedule IV controlled substance
   d. An exempt prescription product

4. When utilizing a single-copy DEA Form 222 to order Schedule II controlled substances, who is responsible for making a copy of the form?
   a. The supplier
   b. The purchaser
   c. The DEA
   d. The PDMP manager

5. The daily sales purchase limit for pseudoephedrine products is
   a. 0.6 g of base product
   b. 2.6 g of base product
   c. 3.6 g of base product
   d. 120 tablets

6. Consultant pharmacists are required to perform a medication regimen review for long-term care patients
   a. When requested by the facility
   b. At least weekly
   c. At least every 30 days
   d. When a medication error occurs

7. Dr. Costa calls your pharmacy and asks if she can call in a prescription for Vicodin for Mr. Garcia, a cancer patient who is well known to you. Dr. Costa states that Mr. Garcia cannot get relief from any other pain medication, and that Mr. Garcia is unable to get to her office to pick up a prescription. She asks if you can fill the prescription and deliver it to Mr. Garcia's house. Which of the following is true?
   a. You cannot take a verbal prescription for Vicodin under these circumstances because Mr. Garcia is not a hospice patient.
   b. You can take the verbal prescription, but Dr. Costa must send you a written or electronic prescription for the Vicodin within 3 days.
   c. You can take the verbal prescription and only dispense up to a 72-hour supply of the medication.
   d. Both b and c

8. Which of the following drugs may be prescribed by a Qualifying Practitioner (DATA-waived practitioner) for treatment of narcotic addiction? **Select all that apply.**
   a. Buprenorphine
   b. A 3-day supply of any narcotic
   c. Buprenorphine/Naloxone combination
   d. Methadone

9. A fire broke out in the front part of Debra's pharmacy, but the flames did not reach the prescription department. Can the drugs still be dispensed?
   a. Yes, as long as the containers are all closed
   b. Yes, unless the drugs are heat sensitive
   c. Yes, but only after notifying patients that their prescription may have been exposed to smoke
   d. No, the smoke from the fire may have adulterated the drugs

10. Sterile preparations must be compounded in a primary engineering control device which is capable of maintaining at least
   a. ISO Class 3 conditions
   b. ISO Class 5 conditions
   c. ISO Class 7 conditions
   d. ISO Class 8 conditions

11. The pharmacy you work at utilizes a separate central processing center and central fill pharmacy. Which of the following locations is responsible for offering counseling to the patient?
   a. The originating pharmacy
   b. The central processing center
   c. The central fill pharmacy
   d. The delivering pharmacy

12. Anabolic steroids are classified under which schedule?
   a. Schedule II
   b. Schedule III
   c. Schedule IV
   d. Schedule V
   e. None of the above

13. Which of the following situations does NOT require a prospective drug review to be performed?
   a. A pharmacist dispenses a drug to a medical practitioner which the practitioner will administer to a patient
   b. A pharmacist fills a prescription for a patient who lives in a personal care home
   c. A pharmacist fills a prescription for a patient in a nursing home
   d. A pharmacist in a hospital pharmacy fills an outpatient prescription for a hospital employee
   e. A pharmacist in a hospital dispenses a drug which will be administered to a patient in the hospital

14. A pharmacist receives an electronic prescription for fentanyl. The pharmacist consults with the prescriber of the medication. After such consultation, which of the following pieces of information may not be added or changed on the prescription even if the prescriber authorizes it?
   a. Patient's address
   b. Patient's name
   c. Drug strength
   d. Prescriber's address
   e. Directions for use

15. A nursing home patient who is prescribed estrogen must receive a copy of the patient package insert
   a. After one week of therapy
   b. Prior to the administration of the first dose and then every 30 days
   c. Annually
   d. If the doctor specifically requests it be given

16. For which class of recall is there a reasonable probability that the product could cause serious adverse effects or death?
   a. Class I
   b. Class II
   c. Class III
   d. Class IV

17. Dr. Galloway writes a prescription for Percocet on July 7, 2022. What is the last day the prescription can be dispensed?
   a. July 14, 2022
   b. August 7, 2022
   c. January 7, 2023
   d. July 7, 2023

18. Place the following in order from the shortest time to the longest time:
   a. Time limit a supplier has to fill an order on a DEA 222 Form for fentanyl.
   b. Time limit for obtaining all authorized refills on a prescription for carisoprodol.
   c. Time limit for obtaining all partial fills of a prescription for methylphenidate if requested by the patient.
   d. Time limit for obtaining a written or electronic prescription after receiving an emergency verbal order for meperidine.

19. Which of the following is NOT a permissible use or disclosure of protected health information under HIPAA?
   a. Providing a list of all prescription medications to a patient's primary care physician
   b. Sending prescription information to a third-party insurance company for payment purposes
   c. Sending coupons for diapers to all pharmacy customers taking prenatal vitamins
   d. Providing a face-to-face recommendation of an OTC product to a patient based on the patient's symptoms and drug allergy profile

20. Pharmacy technicians may: (**Select all that apply**)
   a. enter prescription information in a patient profile.
   b. remain in the pharmacy while the pharmacist takes a break in the mall food court.
   c. print pharmacy labels.
   d. accept new verbal telephone prescription orders.
   e. assist with reconstituting parenteral products.

21. Which of the following products requires a prescription to be dispensed?
   a. Humalog®
   b. Humulin N®
   c. Lantus®
   d. Both a and c

22. Secobarbital in suppository form is classified under what schedule?
   a. Schedule II
   b. Schedule III
   c. Schedule IV
   d. Schedule V

23. Which of the following is not part of the transaction data required to be maintained by a pharmacy when it purchases most prescription drugs from a wholesaler or manufacturer?
   a. Transaction Information
   b. Transaction History
   c. Transaction Statement
   d. Transaction Certification

24. Under the iPLEDGE Risk Evaluation and Mitigation Strategy (REMS) for isotretinoin, the maximum quantity that can be dispensed is a

    a. 7-day supply

    b. 14-day supply

    c. 30-day supply

    d. 60-day supply

25. A patient enters a pharmacy on May 1, 2022, and provides the pharmacy with a new prescription for an antidepressant medication written on February 1, 2022, for a one-month supply with one refill. The patient informs the pharmacist they were waiting to obtain and start the medication until they finished various work commitments that involved a lot of traveling. As the pharmacist was preparing the prescription, they noticed the prescriber on file is one that retired the prior month and is no longer in practice. How should the pharmacist handle this situation?

    a. Provide the patient with the medication with one refill on file to fill prior to February 1, 2023.

    b. Inform the patient they can obtain this first fill, but will need a new prescription for the next fill.

    c. Provide the patient the medication with one refill, but replace the ordering prescriber with another prescriber in the same office as the retired physician.

    d. Inform the patient they are unable to fill the prescription, and offer to contact the patient's new physician about the medication.

    e. Provide the patient with 3 days of the medication and inform her she must obtain a new prescription to receive additional medication.

26. Pharmacist Vincent has some expired morphine tablets he would like to send to a reverse distributor for destruction. What documentation is required to accomplish this?

    a. DEA Form 222

    b. DEA Form 41

    c. DEA Form 106

    d. An invoice

27. A nonprescription bottle of 1 and 1/4 grain aspirin tablets cannot contain more than
   a. 24 tablets
   b. 36 tablets
   c. 50 tablets
   d. 100 tablets

28. A pharmacist received a bottle of generic tetracycline capsules from a wholesaler. The label stated that each capsule contained 500 mg of the drug when it only contained 250 mg of the drug. There was nothing about the drug that would indicate to the pharmacist that this problem existed. The pharmacist dispensed several prescriptions before the problem was detected. Which of the following statements is true regarding the tetracycline?
   a. It is adulterated only.
   b. It is misbranded only.
   c. It is neither adulterated nor misbranded but is instead a minor technical violation of the potency requirements.
   d. It is both adulterated and misbranded.
   e. It is in violation of the Poison Prevention Packaging Act.

29. Which products are required to be dispensed with the warning "Caution: Federal law prohibits the transfer of this drug to any person other than the patient for whom it was prescribed"? **Select all that apply.**
   a. Buprenorphine
   b. Naloxone
   c. Robitussin AC
   d. Lipitor
   e. Klonopin

30. Which of the following is likely to be outside the scope of practice for a dentist to prescribe?
   a. Alprazolam
   b. Amoxicillin
   c. Oral contraceptives
   d. Lidocaine gel

31. Dr. Smith sets up a new private practice near your pharmacy. Soon after, you begin to receive several prescriptions for methadone written by Dr. Smith. You call Dr. Smith and she explains to you that she is treating patients for opioid addiction. You should

a. Document this conversation and continue to fill the methadone prescriptions.

b. Ask Dr. Smith for her Drug Addiction Treatment Act (DATA) waiver identification code or "X" number and continue to fill the methadone prescriptions.

c. Explain to Dr. Smith that she cannot prescribe methadone to treat opioid addiction, and that you must refuse to fill any further prescriptions for methadone from Dr. Smith.

d. Fill prescriptions for methadone 10 mg from Dr. Smith but refuse to fill prescriptions for methadone 40 mg.

32. On September 3, 2022, Dr. Galloway issues three prescriptions to Sally for Adderall. Each prescription is for a 30-day supply. The prescriptions are each written on separate prescription forms and all are dated September 3, 2022. Prescription #1 contains no additional instructions. On Prescription #2, Dr. Galloway writes, "Do not fill before October 1, 2022." On Prescription #3, Dr. Galloway writes, "Do not fill before November 1, 2022." Which of the following is true?

a. Dr. Galloway cannot postdate Schedule II controlled substance prescriptions in this manner; therefore, Prescription #2 and Prescription #3 are not valid.

b. All the prescriptions are valid and the earliest fill dates must be followed.

c. None of the prescriptions are valid because Adderall cannot be prescribed on written prescriptions.

d. None of the prescriptions are valid because Adderall can only be prescribed for a 10-day supply.

33. A pharmacist receives prescriptions for 12 different patients from the same physician over a 3-hour period. All of the prescriptions are written for patients from out of state and for the same combination of Vicodin, Xanax, and Soma. Which of the following are true? **Select all that apply.**

a. If the pharmacist confirms that the physician has a valid license and DEA number, the prescriptions are likely valid and can be filled.

b. If the pharmacist calls the physician and the physician confirms that he or she wrote the prescriptions and saw the patients, the prescriptions are likely valid and can be filled.

c. The prescriptions are not likely to be valid because they appear to have not been issued for a legitimate medical purpose.

d. If the pharmacist fills the prescriptions, he or she could be subject to disciplinary action by the state board of pharmacy.

34. Pharmacist Fred believes that customers would like to buy small quantities of nonprescription drugs and decides to repackage bottles of 100 ibuprofen 200 mg tablets into amber prescription vials of 10 tablets and then sell them to the public. The vials are labeled with the name of the drug, the manufacturer, the lot number, and the expiration date from the original bottles. Which of the following statements are true? **Select all that apply.**

a. Pharmacist Fred can repackage in this manner because it is for his own use in the pharmacy.

b. Pharmacist Fred has misbranded the ibuprofen.

c. The repackaging by Pharmacist Fred is considered compounding and within the practice of pharmacy.

d. The repackaging by Pharmacist Fred is considered manufacturing.

35. For which of the following prescriptions can a fax serve as the original prescription?

a. A prescription for Demerol tablets for a 30-year-old postal worker

b. A prescription for Ritalin tablets for a 12-year-old boy who lives with his parents

c. A prescription for methamphetamine tablets for a 78-year-old LTCF patient

d. A prescription for a morphine injection for an 86-year-old hospice patient

e. Both c and d

36. All partial dispensings of Schedule II controlled substances for a nursing home patient must be completed within
    a. 72 hours
    b. 7 days
    c. 30 days
    d. 60 days

37. When is a dispenser required to query the PDMP?
    a. Prior to dispensing any opioids
    b. When patients obtain benzodiazepines from multiple prescribers
    c. Prior to refilling CIII medications for existing patient
    d. Existing patients using insurance coverage for a new CII prescription

38. Which of the following is true regarding a pharmacy that is an Authorized Collector?
    a. The inner liner of a collection receptacle must be removed by or under the supervision of at least two employees of the pharmacy.
    b. The inner liner of a collection receptacle may not be removed by employees of the pharmacy.
    c. The contents in a collection receptacle must be inventoried before being destroyed or being sent for destruction.
    d. Collection receptacles may be placed anywhere within the pharmacy.

39. Which of the following statements regarding pharmacist management of drug therapy is correct?
    a. When authorized, pharmacists may prescribe medications, adjust a drug regimen, and administer medications
    b. Management of drug therapy is only permitted in institutional settings
    c. Written protocols and collaborative agreements are effective for at least 3 years
    d. Notification of permitted activities is required to be communicated to the authorizing physician within 72 hours

40. Which OTC product label must contain a warning about liver toxicity?
    a. Nonsteroidal Anti-Inflammatory Drugs (NSAIDs)
    b. Phenacetin
    c. Acetaminophen
    d. Ipecac Syrup

41. A prescriber orders a female patient a month's supply of birth control pills and states refills are "prn." How should the pharmacist address this?
   a. Enter unlimited refills for the prescription and tell the patient refills will only end after the prescriber informs the pharmacist to no longer fill any.
   b. Enter refills for the prescription with an expiration of 1 year from the issuance date.
   c. Enter 5 refills on the prescription and tell the patient they will need to obtain a new prescription once those 5 refills are complete or after 6 months, whichever comes first.
   d. Decline to fill the prescription and tell the patient the prescriber has to specify a specific number of refills for the prescription to be valid.

42. A physician assistant would like to start a patient on Ritalin. What is the maximum days' supply that the physician assistant can prescribe for the patient at this time?
   a. 3 days
   b. 7 days
   c. 30 days
   d. There is no limit

43. Which of the following may be in possession of prescription drug samples? **Select all that apply.**
   a. A hospital pharmacy that has been requested to maintain samples by a physician associated with the hospital
   b. A physician assistant who has prescriptive authority in a state
   c. A community pharmacy located in a medical office building that has been requested to maintain samples by the physicians located in the same building
   d. A mail-service pharmacy

44. An outsourcing facility must report serious adverse effects related to any drug they produce within
   a. 3 days
   b. 10 days
   c. 15 days
   d. 20 days

45. Which of the following products are exempt from the requirements of the Poison Prevention Packaging Act? **Select all that apply.**
  a. Isosorbide dinitrate 2.5 mg chewable tablets
  b. Nitroglycerin 2.5 mg extended release capsules
  c. Isosorbide dinitrate 10 mg tablets
  d. Nitrostat 0.4 mg sublingual tablets

46. Which of the following is true regarding refill reminder programs?
  a. Since the purpose of these programs is to encourage the sale of future prescriptions, they are considered marketing programs and require a HIPAA authorization from the patient.
  b. If the refill reminder program is for prescription drugs currently prescribed for a patient, they are considered treatment and do not require a HIPAA authorization from the patient.
  c. Refill reminders may not be sent via text message.
  d. Refill reminders are not allowed for controlled substances.

47. You receive a prescription calling for you to compound and dispense a one-pint bottle of a solution containing 120 mg of acetaminophen and 16 mg of codeine per teaspoon mixed with cherry flavoring. What schedule would this product be in?
  a. Schedule II
  b. Schedule III
  c. Schedule IV
  d. Schedule V

48. What information is required to be documented by the pharmacist receiving a transferred prescription? **Select all that apply.**
  a. Date of issuance of original prescription
  b. Complete refill record
  c. Original numbers of refills authorized on prescription
  d. Pharmacist name and license number from pharmacy it was transferred from

49. You work in a community pharmacy across the street from a large teaching hospital. You receive a prescription for Percocet written for a 12-year-old child who was seen in the emergency room of the hospital. The prescription is written by Dr. Anh, an internal medicine resident at the hospital, on a hospital prescription pad, and has the hospital's DEA number followed by "A16." Which of the following is true?
    a. A prescription for Percocet for a 12-year-old child cannot be dispensed.
    b. The prescription is valid but may only be dispensed by the hospital's outpatient pharmacy.
    c. The A16 is an indication that only a quantity of 16 may be dispensed.
    d. The prescription may be filled at your pharmacy.

50. Which of the following statements regarding emergency refill prescriptions is correct?
    a. A pharmacist can dispense an emergency refill prescription for controlled and non-controlled medications
    b. A pharmacist can dispense up to a 30-day supply emergency refill prescription for a medication not available to be dispensed in a 72-hour supply
    c. A pharmacist can only dispense emergency refill prescriptions for acute medical conditions
    d. A pharmacist is to notify the prescriber of dispensed emergency refill prescriptions within 48 hours

51. DEA Form 41 would be used to document which of the following? **Select all that apply.**
    a. Destruction of expired Demerol tablets in a hospital pharmacy
    b. Wasting of a partial quantity of a morphine 10 mg ampule in a hospital
    c. Destruction of controlled substances from a collection receptacle by a pharmacy that is an authorized collector
    d. Sending an expired bottle of tramadol to a reverse distributor

52. Which of the following is true regarding DEA Form 106?
    a. It should be used to document waste of a controlled substance.
    b. It must be signed by two witnesses.
    c. It must be sent to DEA within one business day of discovery of a significant loss or theft of controlled substances.
    d. It must be used to report any theft of a controlled substance.

53. When dispensing generic medications, which of the following statements is correct?
- **a.** Narrow Therapeutic Index drugs are automatically considered generically equivalent drugs
- **b.** Only prescribers can request pharmacists to not dispense generic medications
- **c.** Patients do not have to be notified regarding generic substitution or the price difference
- **d.** Refills using a different generic product requires patient and prescriber notification or authorization

54. Which of the following information is required on the pharmacy label of a dispensed prescription medication? **Select all that apply.**
- **a.** Pharmacy name and address
- **b.** Patient's birthdate
- **c.** "Do not use after (manufacturer's expiration date)" if date is less than 1 year
- **d.** If a generic is dispensed, the generic name and manufacturer
- **e.** Patient's address

55. Emergency medication kits:
- **a.** are prohibited by federal law to be used at facilities without an on-site pharmacy.
- **b.** are to be stocked by the hospital pharmacy.
- **c.** are not permitted to be placed at long-term care facilities.
- **d.** can only be accessed by a pharmacist.

56. Compounding sterile antineoplastic agents must comply with which of the following USP chapters?
- **a.** USP 795 and 1161
- **b.** USP 795 and 800
- **c.** USP 797 and 800
- **d.** USP 797 and 1161

57. Pharmacist Kurt reconstitutes a pharmacy bulk package of vancomycin to make a batch of 10 IV bags for dispensing today. What is the risk level of the batch of preparations he is compounding?
- **a.** Immediate Use
- **b.** Low Risk
- **c.** Medium Risk
- **d.** High Risk

58. A pharmacy is required to
   a. be at least 250 square feet in size.
   b. have a prescription counter of least 10 linear feet in length and 2 linear feet in width for up to 2 pharmacists working at the same time
   c. display licenses/permits in a conspicuous place in the pharmacy.
   d. all of the above

59. Pharmacist Kevin is preparing the Assessment of Risk required by USP 800 to identify the hazards and mitigating strategies for his health system. Which organization maintains the list of drugs that are hazardous to healthcare personnel?
   a. National Association of Boards of Pharmacy
   b. American Pharmacists Association
   c. Occupational Safety and Health Administration
   d. National Institute of Occupational Safety and Health

60. Which of the following statements regarding discipline of a pharmacist is correct?
   a. A pharmacist disciplined in another state must report this to Pennsylvania within 30 days
   b. Suspensions of a pharmacist can only occur after the pharmacist has received their due process regarding hearings
   c. Grossly unprofessional conduct cannot result in discipline
   d. Revocation of a pharmacist's license is permanent, and one is barred from applying for reinstatement in the future

EXPLANATORY ANSWERS

1. **A. and B.**
   This product is illegitimate under the Drug Supply Chain Security Act (DSCSA). Both A. and B. are obligations of a pharmacy under the DSCSA once an illegitimate product is identified. C. is incorrect because although a recall may be initiated, that is not the obligation of the pharmacy. D. is incorrect because the DSCSA is enforced by FDA, not DEA.

2. **D.**
   A Patient Package Insert is required for oral contraceptives and estrogen products, not OTC products.

3. **B.**
   Fiorinal® (butalbital, aspirin, and caffeine) is a Schedule III controlled substance, as is Fioricet® (butalbital, acetaminophen, caffeine) in Pennsylvania.

4. **B.**
   With a single-copy Form 222, the original form must be sent to the supplier, so the purchaser has to make a copy for their records before placing the order. This is required to be able to document the controlled substances that are received on the copy.

5. **C.**
   Under the Combat Methamphetamine Epidemic Act and the PCSDDCA, the daily sales limit for pseudoephedrine base product is 3.6 grams per day.

6. **C.**
   CMS requires a consultant pharmacist to perform a medication regimen review every 30 days and must report any irregularities to the attending physician, the facility's medical director, and the facility's director of nursing.

7. B.

This qualifies as an emergency situation where a pharmacist can take a verbal order for a Schedule II drug. One of the requirements to do this is that the prescriber must send an electronic or written prescription for the Schedule II drug within 3 days (don't confuse this with federal law, which is 7 days). There is not a requirement that the patient be in hospice. Furthermore, the amount that can be dispensed under an emergency verbal order for a Schedule II drug is the amount necessary to treat the patient during the emergency. It is not necessarily a 72-hour supply, which is often confused as the requirement (and may be in other states).

8. A. and C.

A Qualifying Practitioner (DATA-waived practitioner) can only prescribe two drugs to treat narcotic addiction: buprenorphine and buprenorphine/naloxone combination. While they may be able to prescribe other narcotics, including methadone for pain control, no prescriber may prescribe those products to treat narcotic addiction.

9. D.

Remember that a drug can be adulterated, even if the container it was in is sealed, if it has been held under conditions where it may have been contaminated. The fact that the product was exposed to excessive heat and/or smoke is enough to make the product adulterated.

10. B.

Primary engineering control (PEC) devices must be capable of maintaining ISO Class 5 air quality. You should also be familiar with ISO Class requirements for anterooms and buffer rooms.

11. D.

PBOP rules require the delivering pharmacy to make the offer to counsel.

12. B.

Anabolic steroids are Schedule III controlled substances under federal and Pennsylvania law.

13. A.

Prospective drug reviews are not required when a physician dispenses a drug to a patient being treated in the emergency room, a pharmacist dispenses a radiopharmaceutical to a physician who will administer it to a patient, a medical practitioner dispenses a drug, a pharmacist dispenses a drug to a medical practitioner which the practitioner will administer to a patient, and when a pharmacist delivers naloxone to an employee of a correctional facility, prison, jail, or residential drug treatment facility for an individual pending release.

14. B.

Most things can be added or changed on an electronic Schedule II prescription by calling the prescriber and documenting the conversation and additions/changes on the prescription. However, adding or changing the name of the person for whom the prescription was prescribed is not something that can be added or changed, even by calling the prescriber. It would require a new electronic prescription.

15. B.

Institutionalized patients prescribed an estrogen or oral contraceptive, including nursing home and hospitalized patients, are supposed to be given a patient package insert prior to receiving the first dose and every 30 days thereafter. This is one of those things that does not often happen in practice but is technically required under federal rules.

16. A.

Class I recalls are the most serious recalls, and are those in which there is a reasonable probability of serious adverse effects or death.

17. C.

Schedule II prescriptions in Pennsylvania cannot be filled more than 6 months from the date of the prescription. The pharmacist should use professional judgment in determining if this would be appropriate.

18. D.—Time limit for obtaining a written or electronic prescription after receiving an emergency verbal order for meperidine (3 days)

C.—Time limit for obtaining all partial fills of a prescription for methylphenidate if requested by the patient (30 days)

A.—Time limit a supplier has to fill an order on a DEA 222 Form for fentanyl (60 days)

B.—Time limit for obtaining all authorized refills on a prescription for carisoprodol (6 months)

19. C.

Sending diaper coupons to patients taking prenatal vitamins would be considered marketing because you are using the patients' protected health information (i.e., the fact that they are taking prenatal vitamins) to try to sell them a product—diapers. Sending a physician a list of a patient's medications fits within the treatment definition under HIPAA and does not require a patient's consent. Sending information to a third-party insurance plan is part of payment. Although recommending an OTC drug product sounds like it could be considered marketing, HIPAA has a specific exemption that allows this.

20. A., C., and E.

A pharmacy technician is permitted to do the activities listed in A., C., and E. under the direct supervision of a pharmacist. The pharmacy technician may stay in the pharmacy when the pharmacist is on a break, but the pharmacist must remain within the immediate building. A pharmacy technician is also prohibited from taking verbal orders.

21. D.

Both Humalog® and Lantus® are brands of insulin that require a prescription. Be sure to know those that require a prescription and those that do not.

22. B.

Secobarbital in suppository form is Schedule III, but in other dosage forms is Schedule II.

23. D.

Under the DSCSA, Transaction Data that must be provided for each purchase of a drug includes a transaction history, transaction statement, and transaction information. It does not include a transaction certification.

24. C.

The iPLEDGE Risk Evaluation and Mitigation Strategy (REMS) for isotretinoin is one of the most common REMS, and you should know the details of this program, including the limitation of a 30-day supply.

25. D.

The current PBOP rule states that no prescription may be knowingly filled or refilled for a patient whose prescription was written for prior use by a prescriber who is deceased or no longer in practice. While this may not seem like the best answer regarding patient care, it does comply with the PBOP rule.

26. A.

This is a transfer from one DEA registrant (the pharmacy) to another DEA registrant (the reverse distributor). Since morphine is a Schedule II drug, all transfers of Schedule II drugs must be made using DEA Form 222. DEA Form 41 is not used because the pharmacy is not destroying the drug. An invoice would be the correct answer if the drug involved were a Schedule III–V product.

27. B.

This is from those sets of federal regulations that apply to certain OTC products that include special labeling requirements. Within those rules are special requirements for pediatric (1 and 1/4 grain) aspirin tablets that restrict sales to bottles of no more than 36 tablets. It also requires a warning regarding Reye's syndrome.

28. D.

Remember that when the label states something that is false or misleading, the product is misbranded. Here, the product lists one strength but inside the bottle is a different strength, so the product is misbranded. However, because this involves the strength of the product, it is also adulterated because the definition of adulteration includes when the drug's quality or strength falls below that which it represents.

29. A., C., and E.

This is one of those tricky questions because most pharmacies put this warning on every prescription label, but it is only required for Schedule II–V controlled substances. A., C., and E. are all controlled substances. While the warning is not required for Schedule V products under federal law, it is required in Pennsylvania.

30. C.

A dentist can only prescribe drugs that are related to the practice of dentistry, and it is not likely that would include prescribing oral contraceptives.

31. C.

While methadone can be used to treat opioid addiction, it cannot be prescribed by a practitioner or dispensed by a pharmacy for this purpose. It can only be provided at a narcotic treatment center, and a pharmacy is not registered as a narcotic treatment center. A DATA-waived practitioner also cannot prescribe methadone for the treatment of opioid addiction. They can only prescribe buprenorphine and buprenorphine/naloxone combination. Do not get narcotic treatment centers confused with DATA-waived practitioners.

32. B.

The issuance of multiple Schedule II prescriptions on the same date is permitted by DEA if the subsequent prescriptions indicate the earliest fill date and the total quantity prescribed does not exceed a 90-day supply. While Pennsylvania does require electronic prescriptions for controlled substances, there are exceptions so one may still see written prescriptions. There is also no federal or Pennsylvania law that restricts the quantity of a Schedule II prescription to a 10-day supply.

33. C. and D.

This is a clear example of a situation which requires a pharmacist to exercise their corresponding responsibility to ensure that controlled substance prescriptions are being issued for a legitimate medical purpose and in the usual course of professional practice. Simply relying on the fact that the prescriber has a valid DEA number, or even calling the prescriber to confirm that the patients were seen, is not enough to clear the numerous "red flags" in this situation. The prescriptions are not valid, and a pharmacist could face disciplinary action if he or she fills these prescriptions.

34. B. and D.

The repackaging of drug products, including OTC products, is considered manufacturing by the FDA. The products would be misbranded because they do not contain all the required information on the label of an OTC product as required by FDA. While FDA does recognize some exceptions that allow pharmacists to prepackage drugs for their own use, such as packaging into unit-dose or compliance packaging, it does not include the repackaging of OTC products that are sold to the public.

35. E.

Pennsylvania requires Schedule II prescriptions to be electronic but permits written under certain circumstances. Fax prescriptions are generally treated like verbal prescriptions and are not valid for Schedule II drugs. However, Pennsylvania and DEA recognize a few exceptions to this rule, which includes any Schedule II drug for patients in long-term care facilities and Schedule II narcotics for patients in hospice. Neither of the prescriptions for Demerol tablets or Ritalin tablets meet the exceptions.

36. D.

The time limit for obtaining all partial fills of Schedule II prescriptions depends on a few factors. If the pharmacist is unable to dispense the full quantity, then the remaining amount must be dispensed within 72 hours. If the patient or prescriber requests a partial fill, the remaining quantity must be dispensed within 30 days. If the patient is in a long-term care facility or has a terminal illness, the remaining quantity must be dispensed within 60 days. Remember, these are not refills.

37. B.

The PDMP must be queried when a patient is getting opioid drug products or benzodiazepines from more than one prescriber. Other mandated situations include when the patient is new to the pharmacy, when the patient pays cash when they have insurance, and when the patient requests an early refill.

38. A.

The inner liner of a collection receptacle for drugs must be removed by or under the supervision of at least two employees of the pharmacy. The drugs placed into a collection receptacle should not be inventoried, counted, handled, or removed by anyone at the pharmacy. Collection receptacles must be in the immediate proximity of the pharmacy department. They cannot be placed anywhere.

39. D.

Activities that are permitted must be communicated within 72 hours. Pharmacists do not have prescriptive authority, management of drug therapy may occur in additional practice settings, and agreements are only valid for up to 2 years at a time.

40. C.

See Chapter 2 on special warning requirements for OTC drugs.

41. B.

Prescriptions for non-controlled medications can be refilled for 1 year from the date of the prescription if refills were authorized. This includes "prn" refills.

42. A.

A physician assistant may prescribe a Schedule II controlled substance for initial therapy, up to a 72-hour dose. The prescription must clearly state on its face that it is for initial therapy.

43. A. and B.

Under the Prescription Drug Marketing Act, pharmacies are prohibited from having samples of prescription drugs. There is an exception for hospital pharmacies that are storing prescription drug samples on behalf of physicians affiliated with the hospital. Just having a pharmacy in a medical office building does not qualify for this exception. If a prescriber such as a physician assistant has the authority to prescribe prescription drugs in a state, he or she can also request and store prescription drug samples.

44. C.

Outsourcing facilities must report serious adverse effects to the FDA for any drug they produce within 15 days. *See discussion on outsourcing facilities in Chapter 1.*

45. A. and D.

This question points out that you must know the details of the exemptions under the Poison Prevention Packaging Act, as even the same products may not be exempt depending on the strength and/or dosage form.

46. B.

HIPAA allows refill reminders for drugs a patient is currently taking or was taking in the last 90 days. This falls under the treatment exception under HIPAA, so it is not considered marketing. There is no federal or Pennsylvania restriction regarding refill reminders for controlled substances.

47. B.

Always check to be sure the narcotic substance, codeine in this question, is being compounded with another therapeutic ingredient first because if it is not, the answer will be Schedule II, regardless of the concentration. In this case the codeine is being compounded with acetaminophen, so you need to calculate the concentration of codeine, which for this example is 16 mg/5 ml (teaspoon) or 320 mg/100 ml. This is greater than the maximum concentration for Schedule V of 200 mg/100 ml and less than the maximum concentration for Schedule III of 1.8 g/100 ml, so this is a Schedule III prescription.

48. A., B., and C.

Transferred prescriptions must include date of issuance of original prescription, date or original filing of the prescription, original number of refills authorized, complete refill record, number of refills remaining, location and prescription number of the pharmacy it is being transferred from, and the name of the pharmacy and pharmacist that it was transferred from. The pharmacist's license number is not required.

49. D.

An intern or resident in a hospital can issue controlled substance prescriptions using the hospital's DEA registration as long as it is for a patient that was treated at the hospital and the hospital uses a code or suffix on the DEA number to identify who the prescriber is. That is the A16 in this question. These prescriptions are valid and can be dispensed by any pharmacy, not just the hospital outpatient pharmacy.

50. B.

Emergency prescription refills are not permitted for controlled substances. The maximum quantity allowed is a 72-hour supply; however, if the medication can't be dispensed that way, then it can be a quantity of a month's supply (e.g., insulin). The medication must be prescribed for a chronic condition, and the pharmacist has to inform the prescriber within 72 hours.

51. A. and C.

DEA Form 41 is used to document the destruction of a controlled substance on the premises, but it is also used to document the destruction of a controlled substance from a collection receptacle if a pharmacy is an Authorized Collector. It is not used to document a transfer to a reverse distributor or for wasting a partial quantity.

52. D.

DEA Form 106 is used to document a theft or significant loss of controlled substances. While an initial notice to DEA must be made in writing within one business day of discovery, this does not mean the DEA 106 has to be completed by then. A pharmacy may need time to investigate the extent and scope of the theft or loss because DEA Form 106 requires listing each controlled substance that was lost or stolen, and that may take some time. No witnesses are required to sign DEA Form 106.

53. D.

Refills using a different generic product require patient and prescriber notification or authorization. Patients can also request the brand name to be dispensed. Pharmacies must notify patients of the generic being dispensed and the price difference. Also, NTI drugs are excluded from the definition of a generic equivalent drug.

54. A., C., and D.

The patient's birthdate and address are not required on the label. In addition to A., C., and D., the telephone and DEA number of the pharmacy, the name of the patient, directions for use, name of the prescriber, prescription number and original/refill date, and the name of the drug/strength/dosage form/quantity dispensed are also required. The "Caution" warning is also required on controlled substances.

55. B.

Emergency medication kits in hospitals are to be stocked by the hospital pharmacy. LTCFs must have an emergency medication kit available. Also, other approved practitioners are permitted to access the kits.

56. C.

Compounding sterile hazardous drugs must comply with both USP 797 and 800.

57. C.

A pharmacy bulk package is a conventionally manufactured dosage form. Any batch from all sterile components is a medium-risk preparation.

58. D.

To obtain and maintain a pharmacy permit, all the answers listed must be met. This includes the pharmacy and the pharmacy counter being a minimum size and licenses/permits being displayed properly.

59. D.

NIOSH is the organization that maintains the list of drugs that are hazardous to healthcare professionals.

60. A.

Pharmacists must report discipline from another state within 30 days. There are also limited circumstances where the pharmacist's license can be temporarily or automatically suspended prior to due process hearings. Revocation in Pennsylvania does allow for one to reapply for licensure after a specific time has passed.